A DRUNKING PROBLEM

UNDERSTANDING ADDICTION AND RECOVERY

2nd Edition

Richard M. Prodey

Maryland Affiliate – National Council on Alcoholism and Drug Dependence (NCADD-MD)

ISBN

Published by Maryland Affiliate- National Council on Alcoholism and Drug Dependence
28 East Ostend Street • Suite 303• Baltimore, MD 21230

Printed by Signature Book Printing, www.sbpbooks.com

National Council on Alcoholism and Drug Dependence Inc. • Maryland Chapter
28 East Ostend Street • Suite 303 • Baltimore, MD 21230 • 410-625-6482 phone •410-625-6484
fax • www.ncaddmaryland.org

Who is NCADD-Maryland

The Maryland Chapter of the National Council on Alcoholism and Drug Dependence (NCADD-Maryland) is a statewide organization whose mission focuses on increasing the availability of, and access to, effective prevention, intervention treatment and recovery services in Maryland, education and information dissemination to increase public knowledge and acceptance of addiction as a chronic disease, and eliminating stigma based attitudes and practices often directed towards persons, and their families, impacted by addiction

What Does NCADD-Maryland Do

- **We advocate for people affected by alcoholism and drug addiction** - NCADD-Maryland **"Addiction Treatment Advocates Committee (ATAC)"** works to build statewide consensus around key substance abuse policy and advocacy issues to ensure that public and private dollars invested in treatment and recovery are used for maximum benefit in support of those seeking to access treatment in Maryland.

- **We offer high quality professional education** - the **"NCADD-Maryland Tuerk Conference".** Each year, over 1200 treatment, mental health, social work and human service professionals from across the mid-Atlantic region convene at the Baltimore Convention Center to hear nationally recognized experts lecture on prevention, intervention, treatment and recovery issues.

- **We provide insight, information and hope to the general public** - through the widely-acclaimed Dick Prodey **"Addiction Education Lecture Series".** Attendees learn about common myths about alcohol and alcoholics, chemical dependency as a disease, the complexity of recovery, attitudes towards addictions and recovery, and the impact of the disease on families. The FREE 8-week series is held every Wednesday from 7:00 to 9:00 pm at the Sheppard Pratt Conference Center, located in Towson, Maryland. For more information, or directions, call (410) 625-6482.

- **We build community for people in recovery** – the **Recovery Council of Maryland** was created to provide a supportive network among recovering people, to link the recovering community with vital services and support, and to give recovering persons a voice in advocating for and influencing public policy that affects them. The voices of those in recovery, and their family members play a pivotal role in ensuring smart public policy decisions relating to prevention, intervention and treatment and recovery support services needs are met, and that stigma often associated with the disease of addiction is reduced, and ultimately eliminated.

- **We support families of people affected by alcoholism and drug addition.** Our **"Family Assistance Network' (FAN)** provides a network of direct assistance and support for families impacted by a loved one's addiction by connecting them to supportive services and educational and informational resources to help family members better cope with, understand and address the devastating effect and consequences of addiction on children, parents, spouses and siblings.

- The NCADD-MD website at www.ncaddmaryland.org offers up to date information on prevention, intervention, treatment and recovery issues in Maryland., along with links to helpful resources, and regular updates on federal, state and local public policy and funding issues relating to treatment in Maryland

DEDICATIONS

To all the Prodeys I know.

To Mike, Sean, Beth, Brennan and T.C. and to all they love.

To Emma O'Connor Prodey who taught me to respect people and truth equally.

To Pam Prodey whose confidence pushed this project, and whose patience then endured it.

ACKNOWLEDGEMENTS

Family and friends have suffered through this book's grass roots research. To say I appreciate their understanding would be an understatement.

My special thanks to those who helped with the first edition, especially Dr. Penelope Ziegler, Jana Carrington and John Beemer, for their suggestions and recommendations, as well as their continuing friendship over these many years.

Lots of others have been subjected to my questions about their experiences with addiction and recovery. Their answers were helpful. Always they were hopeful.

The second edition of A Drunking Problem represents a polishing of all of the chapters in the first edition. In addition, Chapter 4 on the Disease and the chapter called "Addiction" have been reworked in light of recent developments in our understanding of addiction.

Two new chapters have been added. "Complicated Addictions" discusses assessment and treatment when addiction co-exists with, and is complicated by a psychiatric disorder. It also covers a range of other topics: medication, Methadone maintenance and supplemental drug treatment, and chronic health problems among them. A new chapter on "Teen Drinking and Drug Use" discusses the difficulties in assessing addiction in a young person. This chapter covers teenage motivation, looking at three key questions: "Why do kids drink?" "Why do kids drunk?" and "Why do kids do drugs?" The notion that peer pressure is the driving force is simplistic and inaccurate, pretending that there is but one question and that question is answered by a single phrase no matter what the age or sex of the teenager. This chapter also includes recommendations for parents and schools.

My thanks to all who have helped with the second edition: especially to my friends at The Retreat at Sheppard Pratt. Special thanks for the many hours Dr. Scott Aaronson spent combing through the first drafts and to Dr. Tom Frankin for his good advice on drug treatment.

A very special thanks goes to The Board of The National Council on Alcoholism and Drug Dependence of Maryland, especially Hal Hathaway, Rob White, Carlos Hardy, and Cathy Gray, whose support and assistance made this second edition possible.

A DRUNKING PROBLEM

Summary of the Chapters

1

ALCOHOL and ALCOHOLICS

The earth appears flat. It isn't; it's round. The sun seems to move across the sky from East to West. The sun doesn't move; the earth moves. During the Renaissance Period, plump women were considered beauties; they modeled nude, their figures were admired in great paintings. Today they are considered too fat for the centerfold. Alcohol appears harmless, a drink. Yet it is a drug, a serious drug.

Perception: Though subtle, there is a significant difference between understanding that alcohol is a drug, and perceiving it as one. Alcohol is an addictive drug; that has been known for some time now. And yet even today few people think of it as a drug, much less an addictive one. To us alcohol is merely a drink. We see it that way because we use it that way, as a beverage. We behave quite differently around alcohol than we do around other drugs. We rarely refer to drunkenness as "overdose." Whiskey is measured in shots, not doses. When someone is drunk, we hardly ever refer to him as drugged. And if we call someone a "drunk," the phrase is intended to refer to his character, not the condition of his brain. Alcohol is truth serum, we think, and so we believe that intoxication reveals identity, not distorts it. What is closer to the truth is that alcohol causes bizarre behavior, not that it releases underlying bizarre behavior. Alcohol packs a punch precisely because it is a drug. Someone who is drunk is drugged. Gin irritates the brain

1

before it loosens the tongue. It also inflames the liver. Drugs distort the mind; they do not reveal the truth.

Alcohol and Overdose: Although Americans are quite familiar with overdoses resulting from alcohol, they rarely associate "overdose" with alcohol. "Overdose" is linked to heroin and cocaine use, and not because we are more familiar with heroin or cocaine overdoses. "Overdose" is a drug word, and alcohol is not thought of as a drug. In general, Americans do not view even extreme drunkenness with alarm, much less as an overdose. Nearly every one over the age of fifteen can tell an Uncle Harry story from first hand experience. At a family gathering Uncle Harry slurs his word; his eyes are glazed; he falls back in his chair when he tries to stand and staggers when he walks. Uncle Harry does this because he has had too much to drink. His relatives are amused, disgusted or disappointed, but few of them are shocked, and fewer still are frightened. Harry is loaded. That's all. Because his condition is alcohol induced, he is taken upstairs to sleep it off while downstairs the party proceeds uninterrupted. No one treats this as a case of overdose because no one perceives Uncle Harry as using a drug, not a *real* drug, that is. Had Uncle Harry's condition been the result of taking too many tranquilizers, the party would stop, and Uncle Harry would then be rushed to a hospital where relatives would insist that his stomach be pumped. They might even want a psychiatrist called for consultation, and may consider involuntary commitment. Those same relatives, however, would not think of taking Uncle Harry to a hospital because he was drunk. And if they did, none of them would be surprised if told to take him back home. Let Uncle Harry swallow pills, and then his problem is treated seriously.

Alcohol acts on the brain in a complex way. A simple way of understanding intoxication, however, is to liken it to the brain's falling asleep. Step by step, alcohol affects inhibition, judgment, reason, coordination, emotion, muscle control, consciousness, heartbeat and breathing. The word "intoxication" means literally a poisoned condition. But in America, it is barely regarded a drugged condition, much less a poisoned one.

In group therapy, a young woman described her own progressive intoxication due to Methaqualone. One Quaalude relaxed her. The second made her "free." Those feelings intensified with a third pill. With succeeding pills, she was unable to speak clearly, focus her eyes and walk a straight line. Because her tolerance for the drug was quite high, she did not pass out until a seventh or eighth pill. A middle-aged alcoholic had listened to the description, surprised because it sounded just like getting drunk. The man was intelligent. He had been taught that alcohol is a drug, and even claimed to believe that. He just did not *perceive* vodka as like Quaalude. And because he didn't, he failed to see the irony in his insisting that he was an alcoholic, and his Quaalude using group member was a drug addict. To his mind they were different.

The Message: In large measure, schools have succeeded in educating children about the nature of alcohol. Today, sixth graders list correctly its characteristics:

- It is a drug.
- It acts on the brain.
- It is a depressant (long term it's a downer).
- Its action is sedative and hypnotic.
- It is toxic, a poison.
- It is potent.

The school's lessons, however, are quite different from the lessons advertising and the social milieu teach. And those lessons shape perception:

- Alcohol is fun. Drinking is about liberation, friendship, and bonding.

- Alcohol is extraordinary (capable of opposites - elation and sedation).

- The rules governing drug use do not apply to alcohol; alcohol is an exception.

- For men, drinking is manly. Women who drink (provided they do not get drunk) are liberated.

- Drinking is sophisticated and mature.

The result of such conflicting messages is that children grow up knowing that alcohol is a drug, but failing to perceive it as one. Adults should not be baffled if they fail to relate to alcohol for what it is. As youngsters, they were told that alcohol is extraordinary; a beverage they may not drink until they are adults. They are told that it is special; an array of fancy accouterments goes with it. It is harmless. Drunks are, after all, funny. It is near magical in its powers. It picks you up as well as calms you down. And alcohol is associated with the strongest motivational forces we know: friendship, sex, love, bonding, wealth, sophistication, and power.

None of this is taught. Learning happens without words. The message is subtle and silent. But it is pervasive and persuasive. It creates not just a way of thinking about alcohol; it fashions a way of *seeing* it. We learn about alcohol's so called "truths" from the places and times we set aside for drinking. Alcohol lessons speak to us from billboards, television, movies, radio, and magazines. We hear the power of alcohol touted in the music we listen to and the literature we read. We absorb lessons about alcohol long before we drink it, unaware of where, when or how we learned what we learned.

Alcohol Places: Consider, for example, what we attach to alcohol from the places we drink it: in bars, inns and taverns, which suggest camaraderie and fellowship; in night clubs with their bright lights and excitement; and in fancy restaurants. When a society spends lots of money to build places which are used exclusively for a single purpose, that purpose is proclaimed important. We construct bars and elaborately decorate them. The message is unmistakable, so unmistakable that we call the time we spend there "happy hour."

Americans are distressed by the fact that crack houses are in the middle of their neighborhoods and are shocked that drug addicts shoot up in the same block where their children play. When this happens, what they fail to appreciate is that drug use has been going on at the neighborhood tavern for years.

Alcohol Times: The occasions we claim as drinking occasions also teach us how to look at alcohol. It is customary to drink at births, weddings, and deaths. When we come in and when we go out, someone has a drink. We celebrate life transitions by drinking: at graduations, promotions, and retirements. We drink on national holidays: Memorial Day, Labor Day, and the Fourth of July. We drink on religious holidays like Christmas. There are even times alcohol is not merely permitted, it is expected. One could argue a case that Americans have a holiday which is, in fact, a drinking holiday. This holiday's central activity is drinking. During this holiday, out of control drinking is winked at, if not outright condoned. This holiday is not celebrated on the day it occurs; it is celebrated the evening before. It is called New Year, but it is not celebrated with a ceremony designed to evoke a sense of renewal and hope at the break of dawn of the new year's first day. It is celebrated the night before, drinking and partying until after midnight. It is as if it were the ending of the old year, and not the beginning of a new one, which is celebrated on December's last day. And how do we celebrate the new year? New Year is not just celebrated by drinking; it seems reserved for that purpose. It is expected that Americans in large numbers are going to drink too much. Coffee stands have been set up at roadsides for the occasion. Public service announcements advise us not to avoid drinking, but to make coffee the one for the road. January 1st is for football and forgetting - and not just old acquaintances either.

Our tolerance of intoxication is extreme. At what point are we shocked and alarmed at how drunk someone is? When he slurs, sees double, staggers, falls down, or passes out? All these are presented in movies as comical. Nearly all are tolerated at significant celebrations. Our notion about what constitutes inappropriate drinking is quite flexible as well, so much so that it is virtually impossible to find circumstances in which alcohol is prohibited without exception. It is clearly not always forbidden on the job; some employees claim they are encouraged to drink with clients. Not everyone who indulges before noon is considered a problem drinker, not if he is a football fan at a tailgate party. Furthermore, alcohol is not outlawed whenever someone operates heavy machinery; not when the machine is an automobile.

One of the ironic side effects of our society's confusion about what constitutes problem behavior with alcohol is that it helps an already rationalizing alcoholic to delude himself into thinking his drinking falls within the norm. He argues that priests and football fans drink before noon, and so his own morning drinking is not a problem.

Alcohol is Exceptional: A trip to the liquor store should prove how special we consider alcohol. It is packaged in fancy bottles in patriotic (red, white, and blue) and in regal (silver and gold) colors. It is called by an array of special names (Miller High Life, Crown Royal, and Southern Comfort). It is attractively displayed, and marketed to the whole range of society - from good old boys in overalls to sophisticates in tuxedos. There are dozens of glasses of different sizes and shapes from which to drink alcohol. The sophisticated host soon learns that there are particular glasses for beer, special ones for whiskey, and especially fancy ones in which wine is to be served. Even the unsophisticated adult knows that a martini is served in a special glass and decorated with an olive. In fact, there is even a glass with its own name, Pilsner. Alcohol is so special that we baptize glasses for its use.

Alcohol's paraphernalia, decanters, stirrers, napkins, shakers, strainers, are but a few of the accouterments for sale in uptown and downtown stores. And if the word "paraphernalia" surprises us, we need to remember that alcohol paraphernalia has been a popular collectible in our country a lot longer than coke spoons and pot bongs. We even have a "cocktail dress."

Few Americans would agree to allow a citizen who is drugged to operate machinery which weighs a ton, has a guidance system responsive to a one inch movement of the hand, develops seven thousands revolutions per minute within seconds, and moves at speeds exceeding sixty miles per hour. And yet our law permits precisely that; provided the drug is alcohol and provided the level of alcohol in the blood stream is "acceptable." Alcohol is exceptional - literally so.

Drinking Associations, Beer and bonding go hand in hand for
Appeals and Motivations: males. Beer complements hard work, exertion and physical power according to at least one ad whose slogan is "It's Miller time." Wine is marketed as more a lady's beverage, and is associated with sophisticated sexual encounters. There was even an old television ad for a particular wine which came wrapped in a burlap bag. The ad featured a spokesman in a tuxedo at a billiard table making his pitch while a woman in a black evening gown stood behind him, silent and motionless. The woman was present but barely acknowledged, and yet an association was communicated. When a sexy woman tells us that, with Harvey's Bristol Cream Sherry (a brand of wine), "It's downright upright" for a woman to invite a man over for a drink, not many of us recognize that the power to break one of society's unwritten laws is being linked to a brand of wine.

Whiskey ads stress whiskey's association with prestige, power, and position. The clearest example of this is the old "Dewer's Profiles" magazine ads. They highlighted individuals at the top of their professions, who pulled in six figure incomes, did all sort of exciting recreations and who drank Dewers, a brand of scotch.

In 1996, the hard liquor industry ended its voluntary ban on advertising in certain venues; a ban which had been in effect since 1936 for radio and 1948 for television. Since 1996, whiskey ads have been appearing on television with increased frequency. Two factions are at odds on the issue of hard liquor advertising on television. The one, a mix of legislators and special interest groups, is concerned that TV advertising will increase the number of drinkers, especially young drinkers. At the opposing end of the conflict, the hard liquor industry argues for equity in its right to compete with beer and wine makers who have for a long time advertised widely on television. Current TV ads for hard liquor include encouragements to drink responsibly – a praiseworthy gesture in the direction of moderation. What ought to concern us is what sort of associations and appeals these new whiskey ads will play to in our culture.

The Language of Alcohol: Linguists tell us that language
either limits or expands the very
thoughts we are capable of having. In fact, we cannot have a thought
without a word. Language is so potent a means of learning and trans-
mitting perceptions that we must pay particular attention to how we
talk about alcohol. When we do, what we find is that our common
idioms suggest that alcohol is special and that drinking is fun. But,
in the common parlance, we hardly ever refer to alcohol as a drug,
and only in joking do we proclaim it potent. How seriously are we
to take drunkenness when we refer to it as pickled, looped, sloshed,
plastered, bombed, smashed, loaded, wasted, crocked, blitzed, pie-
eyed, shit-faced, and three sheets to the wind?

At Christmas parties hosts ask if their guests would like "a little
something" in their eggnog. It sounds harmless. A glass that needs
refilling with ice and liquor is "freshened up," ironically with a depressant. No bartender keeps his job for long if he asks customers if
they want their "sedative" shaken or stirred, or if they prefer their
"hypnotic" straight up or on the rocks. That well known highball
will never be called a "Seven and Sedative Hypnotic." Would you
like your toxin with a twist?

Despite an American fondness for "telling it like it is," Americans
rarely speak of alcohol bluntly, like it is. Along with caffeine and nicotine, alcohol is legal and socially acceptable (although nicotine has
become suspect recently). So it strikes Americans as extreme to speak
of those drugs as drugs. It is true that people who use alcohol and
caffeine infrequently and in limited amounts appear to take limited
health risks. Some eight or nine out of ten people who drink alcohol
do so without resultant problems. No one expects liquor advertisers
to remind us that their product kills brain cells or is a causative factor
in death from a number of causes. However, as many as 15 percent
of our population who start drinking, begin a process which heads
in the direction of serious health problems, psychological harm, personal loss, insanity, institutionalization, and death. For them alcohol
is the agent of a serious disease. It is a drug for everyone.

A Perception Solution: The American perception of alcohol seems wide, deep and immutable; impossible to change. But our perception of a drug can change, and in fact, within the past twenty-five years, Americans have changed their minds about two drugs. Marijuana, once the drug of jazz musicians and considered exotic and dangerous, has become a teenage recreation, considered relatively harmless by more and more teenagers as well as adults. America *has* changed its perception of marijuana. And Americans have changed their way of looking at another drug, at one time a very popular one. But this time the change is in the opposite direction. Nicotine, within a few years, has gone from classy, sophisticated, and macho to a nasty, smelly habit - and even addictive. Nicotine smokers, once Marlboro men and Virginia Slim women, are virtually ostracized today.

As a society we will appreciate the seriousness of alcoholism as a disease when we perceive alcohol as a potent drug. We will find it easier to regard alcoholics as drugged rather than immature human beings only after we see an alcohol soaked brain as a drugged and poisoned brain. We will recognize that our difficulty accepting alcoholism as a disease is due, in part, to alcohol being both so special and so ordinary a part of our culture. We will appreciate how difficult it is for a recovering alcoholic to refrain from alcohol when we appreciate the special role drinking plays in our society. We will deal effectively with the problems arising from alcohol abuse only if we avoid two extreme views: the one, that alcohol is evil, and the other, that it is innocuous.

Unless societal perceptions change, Americans will be faced with the astonishing incongruity that we remain under-insured for the treatment of what we acknowledge to be the number one health problem and number three cause of death in our country.

2

THE OTHER DRUGGER

The day of the so called "pure alcoholic," the addict who uses alcohol exclusively, will come to an end if it has not already. Treatment centers, which were called Alcoholism Programs in the 1980s, are now called Chemical Dependency Programs or simply Rehabilitation or Treatment Centers. The names changed quite simply because the patients had changed. Any alcoholic under forty years old who has never tried a drug other than alcohol is either lying, been in seclusion, or is in an advanced state of denial. Otherwise he is a dinosaur, a throwback to another era.

Attitudes toward the "other" drugs began changing in the 1960s. By 1990, "recreational" was widely recognized as a term describing both a group of drugs and a way of using them. And attitudes are still changing. Marijuana, at one time depicted as the route to "reefer madness," is considered dangerous today only when it is thought to be a gateway to other drugs. Considered by itself, marijuana is thought to be non-addictive and one of the least problematic drugs. Neither is true. Cocaine's popularity grew steadily into the 1980s, but the deaths of a popular comedian and a promising college basketball star dealt that drug's reputation a serious blow. By the end of the decade, the President of the United States had declared war on it.

Professionals who treat addicts today no longer enjoy the luxury of the simplistic conception in which alcoholics are considered mainstream, while other addicts are thought to be antisocial, bad, or immature. An enlightened view avoids two extremes: that there are no similarities among addicts and that there are no differences among them. For example, nicotine addicts do have something in common with heroin addicts; though the two are not cut from exactly the same cloth.

The Differences: Mood altering drugs differ from each other in several ways. Each produces a pleasurable response as well as unpleasant effects from excessive amounts. Some drugs sedate and are called downers. Others stimulate; they are uppers. A few create mind movies, hallucinogens. Drugs come in nearly every shape, color, and size. Some are liquid (alcohol); some solid (tranquilizers); and some crystalline (cocaine). Some drugs act quickly; cocaine and heroin produce effects within seconds if injected. Others take longer to "kick in." Some drugs produce serious, and in one instance even life threatening withdrawal, whereas withdrawal from other drugs is mild enough for one to go to work and function throughout the day. Some drugs are inexpensive and available twenty-four hours a day, seven days a week, in every neighborhood of every city and town. Others are available only to those with connections and money.

Though mood-altering drugs differ in several ways, drug addicts differ in just a few:

- Their drug of choice (the drug an addict prefers).

- The extent of other drugs used in addition to the drug of choice.

- The individual's drug use style; i.e., the differences in people, places and paraphernalia surrounding his or her use.

- The legality or illegality of the drug and the means of acquiring it.

Alcoholics and "junkies" both break the law, and some are caught at it. One generally recognized difference between a heroin addict and an alcoholic is that the alcoholic breaks the law *after* he is loaded while the heroin addict must break it *before* just to get his supply. A heroin addict, any addict for that matter whose drug is acquired illegally, is forced to break the law and to justify in his own mind doing so. For this reason, individuals addicted to illegal drugs, if not full-fledged antisocial personalities, tend to have an antisocial streak. To the contrary, adult alcoholics acquire alcohol by strictly legal means. Although this does not mean that alcoholics are never antisocial, it does mean that they do not have to do something antisocial just to practice addiction.

As long as certain drugs are illegal and regarded as socially unacceptable, those who gravitate to them will tend to be antisocial. On this point, however, a historical perspective proves quite interesting. The "look" of the typical marijuana user has changed rather dramatically over the last seventy years. The pot smoker of the 1940s seems quite different from the type who smoked that drug in the 1960s. And the 1960s type differs from the 1980s user, who is different yet again from the pot smoker of the 1990s. By the year 2000, marijuana had become a recreational drug for high school sophomores. If some futuristic crystal ball could show us what a typical marijuana addict of the year 2100 might look like if marijuana were legalized today, we might find that he would look quite different from the way we think about present day marijuana users. For that matter, what would the typical alcoholic look like in one hundred years if alcohol were made illegal tomorrow? He might be quite different than the mainstream alcohol user of today.

The Similarities: Beyond the differences among drugs, addiction to the whole range of drugs is remarkably similar:

- Addiction is progressive.
- Its progression is similar regardless of the drug used.
- Addiction changes personality.
- Tolerance for mood altering drugs develops over time.
- Loss of control is a problem with all mood altering drugs.

Excellent summaries of drugs complete with street names, health risks associated with their use, symptoms of dependency, and signs of overdose are available on the internet and from government agencies and local police departments. Keeping these volumes current is a never-ending task since drug inventors regularly create new drugs, and users as quickly coin new names. *Ecstasy,* one of the *designer* drugs, so called because it combines two already familiar drugs (Ecstasy combines stimulant and hallucinogenic properties), is an example of drug maker's ingenuity. *Ice,* a name given to a new form of another familiar drug, crystal Methedrine, is another example of both the producer's and the namer's imaginations.

A Drug and Its Drugger: What health professionals and police departments say about drugs is informative, but not nearly as compelling as what addicts say about them. Their line carries special insights because it reveals as much about *other druggers* and their denial as it does about *other* drugs.

Marijuana and Addiction

Marijuana users, for instance, like to believe that pot is not addictive. They consider it safe for two reasons. First, they claim that they suffer no significant problems from its use, and second, they claim to suffer no profound withdrawal when they stop using. Though it is true that there are pot users who suffer only minimal unpleasant consequences because of the drug, what nearly all marijuana addicts fail to appreciate is how difficult it is for them to quit the drug. Marijuana addiction is subtle. One hardly feels himself a captive of that drug until he tries to quit it. Marijuana addicts ignore too the health consequences, at the very least the damage to their lungs. They are often blind to the fact that marijuana stands inordinately high in the list of their life priorities.

The one symptom marijuana addicts invariably fail to see as serious is their failure to follow through. Though an individual addict may claim, and correctly so, that he has never committed a crime because of pot, what he overlooks is that he rarely follows through on anything because of it.

The emotional flattening that comes with prolonged use of marijuana is another consequence addicts deny. One psychiatrist with years of experience treating addicts refers to it as the *what's the big deal* symptom because chronic pot smokers respond to vital issues with a kind of pervasive emotional flatness. Though their conversation about "head" talk and "head" music can be quite animated, chronic users ask "what's the big deal" about a political election, poverty, nuclear disarmament, war, terrorism, and the state of the economy. One young man whose drug of choice was marijuana reported that the only thing different about him since he started smoking pot was that he "didn't get excited about much any more."

Most significantly marijuana addicts fail to see how their addiction chooses their friends, limits their recreation, dissolves family life, and eventually displaces other interests.

Another curious rationalization for using marijuana is that it is natural; the implication being that what is natural cannot be harmful. Rattlesnakes are natural, but one doesn't play with them.

The myth of the 1960s was that repeated use of marijuana resulted in lowered tolerance so that over time lesser amounts of the drug produced the same or a greater effect, thus making marijuana increasingly economic as well as harmless, if it were true. It is simply not true. Tolerance for marijuana does develop. Today's smoker inhales a more potent joint than was available to him in the 1960s, and because of that, he thinks his use has not increased, whereas he is simply consuming more THC in fewer *joints*. It is the same mistake an alcoholic makes when he thinks he is drinking less because he switched from eight bottles of beer to one bottle of whiskey.

According to a pamphlet published by the American Council for Drug Education, sensitive urine tests can remain positive for the constituents of marijuana for as long as two weeks after a single dose. (Blasinsky & Russell, 1981, p. 6) In treatment centers, metabolites of THC in the urine of chronic smokers have been detected for as many as 28 days, and during that time (even after it) individuals are noticeably affected. How individuals are affected varies. Some are agitated; others lethargic. Some admit to feeling distressed; others think not. Nearly all are startled by how long traces of the drug are detectable.

Educators and parents have reason for concern about the counter-educational effects of a single dose of marijuana because of how long it lingers. At the time in their lives when young people need short memory most of all, pot interferes with that memory. Finally, a few adults persist in believing that abstinence from alcohol and marijuana during adolescence is an extreme expectation. They regard drug use as a rite of passage.

The Addictive Power of Cocaine

Cocaine has been around a long time, and addicts have been teaching professionals important lessons about the addictive power of that drug from their experience with it. Cocaine confirms the suspicion that drugs with the highest potential for addiction are not necessarily those which produce the quickest and most potent physical dependence. Addictive potential is the measure of how seductive a drug happens to be, and how much craving it provokes. Drugs like cocaine have a high potential for addiction because they combine the following characteristics:

- Drugs which act quickly have a higher abuse potential than those which act slowly.

- Drugs that produce an intense euphoria are going to be quite addictive because of it.

- When a drug wears off rapidly, the user must dose more frequently to sustain his high; the drug will appear to that user as controllable and less harmful.

- Some drugs generate powerful cravings which persist for a long time.

- If a drug is perceived as dangerous it will be less seductive than one considered harmless.

Cocaine has the characteristics mentioned. It is a drug used in that one-after-another chain of doses which characterizes addiction. Cocaine, in fact, seems more problematic than either heroin or alcohol. Make no mistake. Alcohol and heroin are pleasurable, abusable, and potentially harmful drugs. But unlike alcohol, cocaine alters one's mood so quickly, especially if injected, and it wears off so rapidly that cocaine packs a double punch. It provides an immediate reward while masquerading as a controllable drug. Also, because cocaine wears off so quickly, users must dose more frequently than with heroin or alcohol. Finally, unlike alcoholics who prefer their booze with sex, cocaine addicts, some at least, prefer cocaine. Any drug that hits you quick, takes you high and leaves you fast, beckons long after it has been discontinued and is thought to be safe, will invite its user to go at it again and again.

"Crack" is concentrated cocaine, ready to smoke. It has been popular because it packs a punch, is relatively inexpensive, and is easy to hide. But crack's popularity is explained only in part for these reasons. Crack is popular in part because its reputation has been as potent as its punch. A drug's reputation, its newness to the drug use scene, cannot be ignored as one of the factors responsible for its popularity, not only among casual users in search of thrills, but among seasoned addicts whose tolerance forces them to find newer ways to get high.

PCP, phencyclidine, was popular for a while. Quaaludes were too. LSD (Lysergic acid diethylamide) was popular in the 1960s, and in new forms, such as *blotter acid* (LSD dropped on blotter paper) and *Ecstasy*. Hallucinogens will every now and then enjoy a comeback with reputations similar to the one they enjoyed in the 1960s. Teenagers rediscover the drug of their parents' generation. It should be no surprise that hallucinogens would regain popularity. Horror stories about LSD died. For a variety of reasons, teenagers consider hallucinogens harmless. And just as with marijuana, teenagers conclude hallucinogens are safer than other drugs. Oxycontin was popular among teenagers leery of heroin, but who enjoyed the narcotic "high." The parade of drugs goes on.

Prescription Addiction

The effects of tranquilizers are so much like the effects of alcohol that Valium, Tranxene, Xanax, Serax, Dalmane, Ativan, and Librium, drugs called Benzodiazapines, are referred to as "freeze-dried" alcohol. A recovering Valium addict (it was the only drug this particular patient had ever used) was listening to a group of alcoholics talk about their drinking escapades. Since her addiction had been practiced behind the closed doors of her suburban apartment, she could not identify with barroom antics or the nightclub scene. She could find no parallel between her solitary use and the fellowship drinkers enjoyed. What she could identify, however, was that alcoholics drank for some of the same reasons she took Valium. She could also discern that the effects of the two drugs were similar enough that she vowed to never to try alcohol because she was sure she would like it too much.

The notion that a prescribed drug is less addicting than one available on the street compares in silliness to the assertions that alcohol would be illegal if the government thought it harmful. An addict is an addict whether he is hooked on a prescription drug, alcohol (which is legal and socially acceptable), or "street" drugs. Mood altering "medicine" can make one as dependent as booze or "junk" can.

One of the differences between alcoholics, junkies and prescription addicts, however, is that prescription addicts do not like thinking of themselves as *addicts*. Denial deludes them into believing that even though they may have lots of trouble stopping the drug, they are not addicted to it. Their denial is supported by the acceptability of their drug and the legal means by which they get it. It appears condoned by the medical profession. A prescription addict reasons that he is not a drug addict since the doctor initiated his drug use. How could anything be wrong with it? And when they need a doctor's help to withdraw from the drug, they consider that a medical problem, not an addiction.

A prescription addict can sustain his addiction for fifteen years and never once break the law to get his drug. Nevertheless, just as with every other addict, prescription addicts must pursue their drug.

And over time that pursuit intensifies. "Scripts" are not pedaled door to door. Doctors do not make house calls surveying which patients need refills. Prescription addicts must seek out, and sometimes con their physicians into prescribing.

Denial also keeps prescription addicts from seeing they love their drugs. That love may be neither conscious nor desired. A prescription addict may resent his dependence on the drug, even hate it. He may concede he needs his drug, but he does not like to think he loves it. But he does love it. He loves its effect. He loves the way it makes him feel. He loves the zone his drug puts him in, and he pursues that zone just like any other addict. Prescription addicts are not unlike the rejected lover who has been abused repeatedly, but who continues to pursue the abusive relationship. When a prescription addict concedes this, he is usually more embarrassed than street addicts or alcoholics, who both more readily admit they love the stuff. At its core, the prescription addict's denial keeps him holding firm to the belief that he is the victim of his condition and not active in its pursuit.

Addictive Potential: Any drug is capable of being abused, even blood pressure pills. Few people abuse antihypertensives, however. Reducing ones systolic and diastolic pressure may be life saving, but it isn't a whole lot of fun. For a drug to have significant abuse potential, it must be one which causes pleasure either because it excites, stimulates, relaxes, or relieves. This is generally true. However, even drugs which are regarded as having a very high abuse potential, such as Percodan, Cocaine, Xanax, or Fiorinal, are not pursued by people who respond to low doses of those drugs in unpleasant ways. Conversely, drugs regarded as having a low potential for abuse have quite a high potential in the hands of the right abuser. Diuretics eliminate fluid from the body and are not a favorite among seasoned addicts (urinating may be a relief, but it is hardly a thrill). In the hands of an anorexic, bulimic, or high school wrestler trying to make weight, however, Diuretics have seductive power. They are abusable.

Drug or Drugger?

Where is addictive potential? Is it in the drug or the drugger? Only as long as withdrawal-producing physical dependence is considered the exclusive criteria for addiction, will we consider potential for addiction a matter of the properties of chemicals. When we realize that addiction actually develops, not just because drugs have power, but because people are attracted to that power, we will grasp addictive potential as involving both the susceptibilities of users as much as the seductiveness of drugs.

Future research will some day confirm that addiction comes about only when the right drug meets the right drugger. Addictionologists know already that though certain drugs are capable of causing dependence in anyone who abuses them, addiction, in fact, does not befall everyone who does use such drugs. Valium has an accepted reputation for addiction and physical dependence. An elderly woman whose doctor put her on Valium during a period of emotional stress, during which she wrenched her back picking up a heavy load of laundry, took two Valiums from a bottle of thirty and stopped. She never took a third. Valium made her groggy. She didn't like it. Her reaction to an addictive drug teaches us something about where we are likely to find the potential for addiction. It is as much in people as in drugs.

Most laymen have little trouble acknowledging that an identical dose of aspirin will affect three people differently. One will take two aspirins and get relief within half an hour. A second has to take three or more aspirin every several hours to get the same relief. A third finds aspirin irritates his stomach so much he refuses to take more than a single aspirin. Antibiotics affect individuals differently. Penicillin works wonders for one person but makes another sick because he is allergic to it. Why should we have trouble accepting that what is true of aspirin, Lithium, and penicillin is also going to be true of gin, Librium, and nicotine?

3

THE PERSONALITY
OF ADDICTION

Examine these dots.

.   .   .

.   .   .

.   .   .

Connect the dots by drawing four straight lines without lifting the pencil from the paper. Try several times.

This game is frustrating, but not because it is impossible, nor because the instructions are a trick. It is frustrating because one perceives the dots in a way that makes connecting them with four lines impossible.

As long as the dots are seen as forming a "box," and as long as one insists on staying within the boundaries of that "box," the problem is unsolvable. The dots are not the problem. It is one's perception of the dots which is the problem. The puzzle is easily solved, but only if one changes his way of *seeing* it.

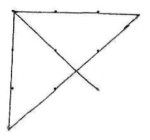

Perceptions of Alcoholism: Alcoholism perplexes us because our ideas about it are based on perceptions that are inaccurate, misleading, or just plain untrue. For instance, if we interpret the behavior of an alcoholic based on the notion that alcohol is truth serum, we are likely to draw conclusions about his personality which are far from the truth. If erroneous ideas about alcoholics form the basis for our ideas about alcoholism, a pair of perceptions misleads us. The notion of an alcoholic personality has been around for so long that people believe that addiction is the result of personality. Despite evidence to the contrary, and despite simple common observation of the variety of types of people who do become alcoholic, the belief persists that an anti-social, arrogant, compulsive, dependent, egotistical, depressed, inadequate, irresponsible, or thrill-seeking person is at risk for developing a drinking problem because of those characteristics. Addicts are easily dismissed as foolhardy, anti-social, and risk-takers if one never actually meets the people who are addicted. It is easy to be misled if one ignores the variety of adult addicts and forgets that many of them got started using drugs at a time when university professors were telling them to "tune in, turn on, and drop out," and that the experience was an exploration of reality, not an escape from it.

Just a couple of generations ago law-abiding citizens broke federal law making "bath tub gin" and weren't considered anti-social because of it. Today, Americans are outraged by even the suggestion that drugs be legalized, overlooking one ironic fact. Except for Prohibition, one of the most toxic of the mood altering drugs, alcohol, has been legal since the country's founding.

If America fails to solve its national problem with drug abuse, it will not be because of overwhelming numbers and insufficient funding alone. It will not be a matter of inadequate health insurance. It will not be a case of too many pushers and too few police. Approaches based on inaccurate perceptions about the basics (such as alcohol, alcoholics, and addicts) are bound to fail.

Myths about Addicts: A myth is particularly good at muddling the truth because a myth is a fiction which is nevertheless deeply believed. Myths form the basis of a good deal of what we think about addiction. Myths abound. A short list reveals some old hangers on and a few new twists on old themes. All are untrue. For example:

- Alcoholics drink a lot. To become an alcoholic one must drink heavily.
- "Hard" stuff is the risky form of alcohol. Stick to beer and wine and your risk is reduced. Mild drugs, such as marijuana, are not addictive.
- People who are dependent on prescription drugs are not real drug addicts. They are just following doctor's orders.
- Alcoholics and drug addicts cannot go very long without drinking and drugging.
- The classic alcoholic is the skid row bum, and the real drug addict injects hard drugs.
- All true addicts inject drugs.
- Morning drinking is hard-core. One who limits his drinking to evenings has no problem.
- Sixteen is too young to be alcoholic.
- Sixty is too old to be a drug addict.
- Real alcoholics drink in binges.
- Addicts mix drugs. Stick to one drug and you're safe.

- Addicts use drugs as a form of protest against society. They act out.

- Alcoholics choose alcohol over the important things in life. They are irresponsible.

- Primary alcoholism is a male problem. Alcoholic women have psychiatric problems.

- Alcoholics are egotists. They put their own pleasure before anyone or anything else.

- Drug addicts go through a phase, which they either outgrow or get hooked.

- One is not addicted until he gets the "shakes."

- Alcohol is truth serum. It reveals personality.

- For the most part, drinking is an escape from reality.

- Teenagers who smoke marijuana are self-medicating an underlying depression.

Definitions of Alcoholism: Very few people bother to write out a personal, formal definition of alcoholism. Yet most people do have a working definition of it. Many times these definitions are based on the mental pictures we have of alcoholics and addicts, and often those pictures come from movies. The problem is that movies depict addicts in extreme ways. That's what sells tickets.

There are formal definitions of alcoholism, and those definitions represent a variety of ways of thinking. Consensus among the experts is hard to come by. But if a single definition were created from only those elements common to all of the expert definitions, what would that composite definition be? How would the popular mythology of alcoholism stack up against it? Here are some expert definitions. With one exception, they are listed from oldest to most recent:

Alcoholism is "any use of alcoholic beverages that causes any damage to the individual or society or both." (Jellinek, 1960, p. 35)

Alcoholism is "an illness, characterized by preoccupation with alcohol and loss of control over its consumption which usually leads to intoxication if drinking is begun; by chronicity; by progression; and by tendency toward relapse. It is typically associated with physical disability and impaired emotional, occupational, and/or social adjustments as a direct consequence of persistent and excessive use of alcohol." (American Medical Association [AMA], 1968, p. 6)

Alcoholism "includes three criteria all of which must be present for the person to be regarded as an alcoholic: (a) large quantity of alcohol consumed over a period of years; (b) abnormal, chronic loss of control over drinking, shown by inability to refrain or inability to stop; and (c) the drinking causes chronic damage to physical health or social standing." (Walgren & Barry, 1970, pp. 716-717)

Alcoholism "includes a condition in which alcohol is consumed to the detriment of a person's health or social functioning over a period of time." (Edwards, Gross, Keller, Moser, & Room, 1977, p. 41)

"Alcoholism is a chronic, progressive, and potentially fatal disease. It is characterized by tolerance and physical dependency or pathologic organ changes, or both - all the direct or indirect consequences of the alcohol ingested. The person with alcoholism cannot consistently predict on any drinking occasion the duration of the episode or the quantity that will be consumed." (National Council on Alcoholism, 1976, p. 764)

Alcoholism is "any use (of alcohol) that interferes recurringly with the person's health, job, or society, including family." (Whitfield & Williams, 1976, p. 7)

Alcoholism is "a chronic, primary, hereditary disease which progresses from an early physiological susceptibility into an addiction characterized by tolerance changes, physiological dependence, and loss of control over drinking. Psychological symptoms are secondary to the physiological disease and not relevant to its onset." (Milam & Ketcham, 1981, p. 170)

Alcoholism is "a chronic disease, or a symptom of an underlying psychic or physical disorder, characterized by dependence on alcohol for relief from psychic or physical distress or for gratification from intoxication itself, and characterized by a consumption of alcoholic beverages sufficient and consistent enough to cause physical or mental or social or economic disability. The dependence is manifested by loss or impairment of control over drinking." (Keller, McCormick, & Efron, 1982, p. 20)

"Alcoholism becomes a disease when loss of voluntary control over alcohol consumption becomes a necessary and sufficient cause for much of an individual's social, psychological, and physical morbidity." (Vaillant, 1983, p. 44)

"Alcoholism is a primary, chronic disease with genetic, psychosocial and environmental factors influencing its development and manifestations. The disease is often progressive and fatal. It is characterized by continuous or periodic impaired control over drinking, preoccupation with the drug alcohol, use of alcohol despite adverse consequences and distortions in thinking, most notably denial." (American Society of Addiction Medicine and the National Council on Alcoholism and Drug Dependence, Inc., 1990, p. 1.)

In reviewing historical definitions of addiction, and in an attempt to clarify the distinction between physical dependence and addiction, The Liaison Committee on Pain and Addiction (a group representing both the world of pain management and the world of addiction) published the following definition in the Journal of Pain and Symptom Management:

Addiction is a primary, chronic, neurobiologic disease, with genetic, psychosocial, and environmental factors, influencing its development and manifestations. It is characterized by behaviors that include one or more of the following: impaired control over drug use, compulsive use, continued use despite harm, and craving (Savage, Joranson, Covington, Schnoll, Heit, & Gilson, 2003, p. 662)

The following definition reflects current thinking at NIDA, (The National Institute on Drug Abuse (2008, What is drug addiction? par. 1) :

Addiction is a chronic, often relapsing brain disease that causes compulsive drug seeking and use despite harmful consequences to the individual that is addicted and to those around them. Drug addiction is a brain disease because the abuse of drugs leads to changes in the structure and function of the brain. Although it is true that for most people the initial decision to take drugs is voluntary, over time the changes in the brain caused by repeated drug abuse can affect a person's self control and ability to make sound decisions, and at the same time send intense impulses to take drugs.

Interestingly, Alcoholics Anonymous never defines alcoholism. What comes closest to a definition is A. A.'s first step of The Twelve Steps (1976, p. 59) , which states, "We admitted we were powerless over alcohol; that our lives had become unmanageable."

How does popular myth compare to these studied formulations? One of the most common myths is that alcoholics drink the "hard stuff" and lots of it. Yet only one of the above definitions mentions heavy drinking. Furthermore, not a single one mentions a particular type of alcohol as necessary to becoming an alcoholic. Morning drinking, according to myth, is what makes an alcoholic, even though the experts are silent on the point. Alcoholics are supposed to love being drunk. They are believed to have been drinkers for many years. The experts, however, do not echo any such sentiments. Many laymen believe that physical dependence is the distinctive criteria of drug addiction, but the experts do not share that opinion. More than a few people believe that personality or family rearing cause alcoholism. The experts do not concur.

Nearly every one of the expert's definitions does contain the seeds of the notion of "loss of control," but that phrase is not defined clearly enough in each instance to determine whether the experts agree on it. One alcoholism thinker uses "primary loss (or impairment) of control" to mean the inability to refrain from a first drink in a drinking episode, and "secondary loss (or impairment) of control" to signify the inability to stop once started (Keller et al., 1982, p. 162). Thirty years earlier, Dr. Jellinek (1960) used the same phrase to mean an alcoholic's progressive inability to control the amount he or she drinks once he begins. And it is the latter notion which the National Council on Alcoholism echoes in its 1976 definition when it says the person with alcoholism "cannot consistently predict on any drinking occasion the duration of the episode or the quantity that will be consumed." Throughout this book *loss of control* is used to mean that phenomenon in which an initial dose of drug sets off a chain of doses which ends in acute intoxication. Early on, alcoholics *lose control* once in a while. In time that problem worsens, and by the end it becomes a consistent pattern. The experts, however, are unclear about whether they agree.

The experts do agree on two points. Alcoholics and other addicts drink and use drugs. Their drinking and drug use causes problems. What emerges as a synthesis of their definitions, once the differences are removed, is essentially what members of Alcoholics Anonymous have said for years. It is not what you drink, how much, how often, where, when, or even why you drink, but what happens as a result of drinking which determines whether you are alcoholic.

A boiled-down, descriptive definition of alcoholism is as simple as this. Alcoholism and/or drug addiction is drinking and/or drug use which causes recurring, significant life problems. "Recurring" is an important modifier because it seems premature to label someone "alcoholic" if drinking has caused only a single problem. "Significant" is another important modifier because most people are unwilling to label someone as alcoholic even if he has recurring hiccups because of drinking.

The definition is descriptive not etiological. It presents a picture of a condition once the condition has occurred without proposing to explain why the condition comes to be. Adhering to a common sense principle that something ought not to be called a problem until it *is* one; this definition suggests that an individual is not called "alcoholic" until drinking causes problems. It sidesteps the issue of whether he is born an alcoholic without excluding the possibility that from birth he or she may be prone to handle alcohol in a way which could lead to problems later in life.

What is an alcoholic? What is a drug addict? An alcoholic is a person with alcoholism. An addict is a person with an addiction. Though admittedly circular, the statement is no more ridiculous than calling a diabetic someone with diabetes. An alcoholic is not a type of personality. He is a person with a type of disease. "Alcoholic" is simply an adjective, the one which refers to a person with a particular disease, alcoholism. "Addict" is the word we use to describe a person who has the disease of addiction. Some day not far off in the future one word may eventually replace the two words, alcoholic and drug addict.

Is there, then, an alcoholic or an addictive personality? Research has answered the question. Dr. Vaillant, in *The Natural History of Alcoholism* (1983, p. 312), summarizes a longitudinal study of several decades by concluding that the so-called "alcoholic personality" is not the cause of alcoholism but the result of it. Anyone who has hung around recovering alcoholics long enough to get past first impressions soon realizes the truth of it. As a group what alcoholics share is not a similar personality, but a similar impact on personality from a similar experience, alcoholism.

If there is an "alcoholic or addictive personality" one has to wonder which it is: composer Wolfgang Amadeus Mozart or composer Ray Charles? First Lady Betty Ford or singer Janis Joplin? All American Jim Thorpe or Saturday Night Live comic John Belushi? Johnny Cash or William Faulkner? Comedian Jack Lemon or W. C. Fields?

Before Alcoholism: Alcoholics report that their personalities were as diverse as any found among members of the human race before alcoholism. Some alcoholics enjoyed well-adjusted, adult success whereas others suffered from serious psychiatric disorders before they started drinking. A portion of those who later became alcoholic had personality problems severe enough to cause difficulty early in life. Some who grew up to be alcoholic were angry youngsters. Others were compliant, and a few were model teenagers. Many alcoholic appear to have had no more than the common problems of adolescence, but those typical problems never had the chance to be typically resolved. Instead alcoholism entered their lives, and as a result maturity didn't. A significant percentage of alcoholics are the products of homes headed by an alcoholic parent and consequently that group had problems before getting sick from their own addictions. Some were normal in every way. Six kinds of people become chemically dependent, each with his or her own problems beforehand:

- Normal people with whatever happens to be life's usual share of difficulties.

- Those for whom addiction started early, cutting short important developmental stages.

- Children of alcoholics for whom dysfunctional family life created problems.

- Youngsters whose childhoods were marked by physical, emotional and/or sexual abuse.

- Character disordered individuals whose personality problems preceded addiction.

- Those with primary psychiatric disorders, such as schizophrenia, depression, or bi-polar disorder.

But chemical dependency, regardless of which drug is used, is a personality changing experience. Varied personalities may enter the process, but personality is subjected to such similar shaping forces that "personality of addiction" does a better job of capturing the relationship of addiction to personality than "addictive personality," which suggests a predictive or causative condition.

An addict who had psychological problems before becoming addicted is sure to be worse off after, but even normal people are changed after a few years. Furthermore, to be subjected to addiction for twenty years, warps personality. What emerges from the bottle ranges not from good to bad, but from bad to worse.

Personality Changing Factors: It is little wonder that addicts end up described as:

- People who are depressed.
- People who are anti-social.
- People who are mistrustful, suspicious, and paranoid.
- People whose emotional lives are restricted.
- People who find intimacy difficult.
- People who have trouble sustaining relationships.
- People who have big egos.
- People who are overly sensitive,
- People who are emotionally labile.
- People who are defensive.
- People with low self esteem.

Addiction changes people.   No single factor produces those changes. At least four powerful forces are at work producing such changes:

- A potent drug acts on the brain.
- The mind is distorted by denial and rationalization.
- Emotions are distorted, dulled and exaggerated.
- The whole process wrecks one's spirit.

The Impact on the Brain: By definition, mind altering drugs affect the mind. They do so in part because they alter the brain. Though each drug has effects characteristic of it, all mood-altering drugs act on arousal centers of the brain, producing alternating states of sedation and irritation. Though in a different sequence, depressants and stimulants both make the brain go "up" and "down." Even heavy smokers are familiar with nicotine's cycles of stimulation, lethargy, and irritation. Quite simply, a drug acts on a brain and that changes personality.

Life Chemically Filtered

Addicts function on a regular, sometimes daily, basis in one of three chemically altered states: elated, sedated, or agitated. To think that someone so regularly altered would remain unchanged is akin to claiming that a patient prepped for surgery with sedative drugs every day for several weeks would be unaffected by the experience. An addict processes life and life experiences through a brain which is chemically affected. The incoming data itself is altered.

Memory Problems

Abusive drug use causes memory problems, and even when such problems are not permanent, a life of forgetting leaves its mark. Non-addicts know how embarrassing it is to forget the birthday of a good friend. For alcoholics, the impact can be gauged by multiplying one forgetting by years of forgettings, and then adding memory blackouts.

Toxic Experience

Some alcoholics think with drugged brains so regularly that they consider drugged thinking normal. And in the final stages of alcoholisms, alcoholics get to join that special group of people who experience the bizarre, the psychotic, and the terrifying. Fears, strange and sudden, visit them. Brains that are poisoned fashion personalities that are poisoned.

The Impact on the Mind: Addiction affects the mind as well as the brain. This happens in several ways, withdrawal being the most dramatic. Anyone who has suffered through acute withdrawal; been delusional, felt his heart palpitate, convulsed, shook uncontrollably, hallucinated or suffered delirium tremens, does not soon forget the experience. It is memorable, in fact, unforgettable. But addiction affects the mind in subtler ways.

Fear of Recurrence and Shame

Long after a withdrawal hallucination has ended, the sufferer harbors concerns about his sanity, fearing he will hallucinate again. For most of her hospital treatment an elderly woman refused to admit that she had hallucinated that water was pouring through the walls of her room because she feared that admitting it would prove her insane and prolong her stay. A middle aged truck driver, hospitalized after he had seen "little black men climbing in his Christmas tree" was still struggling six months later trying to accept the experience as normal for an alcoholic in severe withdrawal. It was more than six months before he was confident he would not hallucinate again. Another patient discharged his pistol at a band of Indians he believed had invaded his living room. He confessed to killing one of them the day he was admitted to the hospital. Later, he refused to talk about the experience as much out of embarrassment as fear. It wasn't until a year later that he could laugh about it.

A Mind Shaped by Denial

For a variety of reasons alcoholics have shameful, silly, bizarre, perverted, frightening, or even psychotic experiences. In order to persist in drinking, they must deny that those experiences are caused by alcohol. Denial will not allow an active alcoholic to blame alcohol, and so he has to find someone or something else to blame. And so he blames his own mind. More than a handful of alcoholics prefer a psychiatric diagnosis as the way to account for their behavior rather than believe the drugs they love make them crazy. Alcoholics are people who spend a lifetime analyzing their personalities, an analysis based on data which they have gathered about a drug-poisoned subject, and yet they believe the analysis to be true because the alternative is unacceptable.

The Effect of Rationalization

Growing tolerance plays a role in changing personality. Tolerance forces an alcoholic to find reasons for why he drinks more and more often. Sometimes he blames others for it. A wife, a lover, a Pope, a president, an evil boss, the Western system, inheritance of a melancholic disposition, an unfortunate childhood, inadequate educational opportunities, too many dependent children, a stressful job, or even a wicked step-mother have been blamed for causing alcoholics to drink. Rationalizing can change minds, and it changes lives, turning friends who confront into enemies. Rationalizing can choose one's friends, end relationships, quit jobs, and alienate friends. It creates a patchwork of distortions, which very likely account for the isolation and loneliness alcoholics end up with.

Prescription addicts must rationalize too. They have to convince themselves that the pain for which they were given a prescription has gotten much worse in order to justify taking more and more potent painkillers. They even invent pain in order to justify needing medication. Ironically, more than a few who have become hooked on prescription drugs started out with legitimate prescriptions for real health problems, but the drugs which originally relieved pain eventually make it worse. Addiction is a trap. Justifying it is another kind of trap.

Projection and Its Effect

Projection is that trick of mind by which an individual sees in others what he is unhappy with and rejects in himself. It too impacts personality. If I believe that drinking is an angry activity in our society when it is really my own angry drinking which is unacceptable to me, that projection will affect me in far-reaching ways. I may end up constructing a philosophy which claims the world to be an angry place, all the while believing that my thoughts are based on truths "out there" when actually their source is in me. And if the world becomes an angry place, it becomes a frightening place too. The denial, rationalizations, distortions, manipulations and exaggerations needed to sustain even an ordinary addiction, if given enough time to work on a personality, are capable of creating the character disorders described in *The Diagnostic Manual*. One need not have a personality disorder at the start of alcoholism to end up with one.

Projection of Self-Mistrust

Addiction is hiding. Even before an alcoholic sneaks a drink, he hides how much he drinks. He hides its consequences. He hides his feelings about it. And he hides the effect it has at home. If others were to see his pain and shame, his loneliness and fear, even he would have to admit that something is wrong. So he hides his feelings. When asked how he feels, he says he is fine even though at that very moment he may be entertaining suicidal thoughts. *What you see is not who he is,* and such duplicity, a calm exterior hiding a turbulent soul, persuades the alcoholic that he is fake, a phony. If then he projects this onto others, he begins believing that everyone fakes it - that no one can be trusted. When addicts hide behind smiles, they find it difficult not to believe that all smiles are masks, and all caring pretense. They learn mistrust.

Shattered Ego Boundaries

One feature of the personality that addiction fashions persuades family members to think that alcoholics have deep emotional problems. It is common for addicts to swing between grandiosity and self-abasement, from arrogance one moment to self-doubt the next, from egotistical to insecure. The mental health professional who is unfamiliar with how common this is may interpret ego vacillations and shaky ego boundaries as indicating a borderline personality, a disorder that can be quite severe. There are alcoholics who are Borderline Personalities, of course, but ego extremes come built into even garden-variety cases.

Bloated, shaky egos are common among alcoholics, and the reason is quite evident when one looks at what happens to an ego during a bout of drunkenness. Anyone with the capacity to drink beyond normal limits without passing out has the opportunity to witness his ego surpass normal limits. On a single night of uncontrolled drinking an alcoholic witnesses his ego flying off in extreme directions: from extremely inflated to extremely deflated. At 9:00 p.m. with a rising blood alcohol level, he sees himself as handsome, wise, strong, witty, powerful, charming, brilliant, insightful and full of genius. By 2:00 a.m. the same fellow who was finding solutions to world problems a few hours earlier now has trouble finding a bathroom to be sick in. The grandeur and humiliation of a single night of such extremes, multiplied by many nights over many years, creates what A. A. members call "an egotist with an inferiority complex." After a dozen years of such bloat and shrink, an alcoholic ends up feeling alternately powerful and useless, simultaneously brilliant, shy and uncertain. Chemical dependency shatters many boundaries. Extreme behavior is common. Ego extremes are run of the mill.

It is axiomatic of chemical dependency, that when one sees the arrogant side of an alcoholic he can assume that beneath lies shaken confidence and shattered self esteem. Conversely, behind a self-abasing exterior often lurks an ego, grand and powerful. Addiction teaches peaks and pits.

The Impact on Feelings: Addiction wreaks havoc on emotional life. Because alcoholics learn their feelings under the influence of a drug, they come to believe that feelings are intense, numbed, exaggerated and agitated, but hardly ever normal. Six beers turn sadness into depression. A pint of bourbon pushes depression to despair and despair to suicidal thinking. Fueled by martinis, anger erupts as rage. Anxiety turns to terror. And it is not just unpleasant feelings that seem out of control; even pleasant ones seem that way. Drunken love comes out as lust, dripping sentimentality or undying loyalty for strangers. Drunken love is as outlandish as drunken anger. Alcoholics either do not feel, or they feel out of control, and so feelings come to be embarrassing and frightening. Feeling itself is mistrusted.

Alcoholics have difficulty in what ought to be the simple matter of naming their feelings. One recovering woman with more than usual difficulty recognizing when she was angry realized that she had equated *real* anger with what she felt when drunk. One night in a drunken rage she shattered a glass shower door with the back of her hand. After that, subsequent anger seemed no match for the memory of blood and glass splattered over bathroom walls. Eventually alcoholics learn to be afraid not just to express feelings, they are afraid to have them. Experience teaches them that to feel is to start a process that will go out of control.

Sudden Feelings

Chemical dependency not only appears to alter moods, it manufactures them. Even in its early stages, chemical dependency generates sudden feelings and changes in feeling states. The following experiences are common even among young addicts. An evening of drinking begins in good humor and ends in tearful self-pity. Intense anger flares out of someone who a minute before was joking. A celebration devolves into melancholy. Unpredictability of this sort makes abnormal drinkers wonder what secrets lie hidden in them, creating all sorts of confusing data to be analyzed the next day while hung over.

A Shame Structured Personality

In addition to the confusion which sudden feelings create, more subtle problems develop over years - guilt and shame the most significant of these. In the thick of addiction an alcoholic feels vaguely uncomfortable about his drinking. As time passes he feels guilty about neglecting others. Later, he comes to be ashamed of not measuring up to his own expectations as well as the expectations of others. As his disease progresses, he suffers unbearable remorse about drunken behavior which can be as bizarre, strange, foolish, cruel and perverted as behavior has ever been.

Guilt and shame are insidious. They begin playing roles long before an alcoholic is "falling down" drunk. One story illustrates the point and is memorable not just because it should have happened only in the movies, but because it illustrates how *loss of control* affects an alcoholic even before he or others realize he has a drinking problem. A handsome and distinguished man had already developed a problem controlling his drinking at a time in his life when he drank infrequently. On one such occasion, at a party in his freshman year of college, alcohol had gotten the better of him before he knew it. At the party there was a stunning young woman this gentleman drinker wanted to impress. He engaged her in conversation and maneuvered her off to the side of a room near a window through which a cool, late summer breeze was blowing. He felt sparkling, debonair and completely impressive, but he was already drunker than he thought, and he was standing next to an open, knee-high vaulted window. With a drink in one hand, he crossed his feet at the ankles and lifted his other hand to lean casually against the wall. He was, however, standing next to the open window. He left the party sooner than intended. After he picked himself out of the bushes, he returned to his dorm, and for the rest of his college career went to great lengths to avoid being seen by the young woman he so wanted to impress. He never dated her. He never had the relationship he had hoped for. Drinking affected more than his dignity. Alcoholism affected him thirty years before he entered treatment for it.   This experience is an extreme one, but common shameful experiences happen to addicts all the time. They slaughter language, embarrass their friends, fall down, make fools of themselves at parties, sneak drinks, and throw up in the midst of company they had hoped to impress. Addiction fashions a personality structured around shameful experiences.

"Next Day Guilt"

An alcoholic is ashamed not only about his drunken behavior, he is ashamed of next day behavior as well. But because he cannot excuse himself the next day by claiming he was drunk, he holds himself fully accountable for it, sometimes harshly so. Addicts begin believing they are just plain mean or bad. What they almost always fail to take into account, of course, is that though they are not drugged the next day, they are still drug-affected; that the alcohol which sedates them Friday night agitates them nearly all of Saturday. Alcoholics are *under the influence* not for just those hours when booze is in the blood stream. They are under its influence, in cases of withdrawal, for days later. Guilt about the "next day" takes years to overcome.

Fear

Addiction serves up extra helpings of fear. Alcoholics fear they will be found out. They are afraid of what they might have said or done in blackouts. Fear turns to paranoia, a paranoia which results from an overblown, overly sensitized ego, from hiding, from fear of exposure, and, of course, from the drug itself. Marijuana makes some of its smokers paranoid. Alcohol makes alcoholics paranoid, and stimulant abusers report feeling intensely suspicious under the influence of those kinds of drugs. But an addict's fears do not start out as full-blown paranoia. At first, he worries he will be discovered as a fraud, that others will see his surface confidence as a sham, and that his facade will collapse to expose him as cruel to those he is supposed to love. Eventually he fears drinking will destroy him, but long before that, other fears are at work. The insidiousness of chemical dependency is that it distorts emotional life so early in the process that drinkers fail to connect their emotional problems to growing alcoholism. Instead they ascribe those problems to personality.

The Loneliness of Addiction

Eventually alcoholic drinking completely isolates an alcoholic. He is lonely because he cannot share his feeling, in part because he is ashamed of them. Addiction breeds loneliness.

A Spiritual Disease: "Spiritual illness" is a difficult concept. A good many people have a tough time accepting such an idea. Human beings already have enough ways of being sick without inventing new ones, for sure. But alcoholism does affect the spirit. A phrase such as "spiritual illness" might well shed a special light on addiction in two ways: 1) it gives a name to the despair addicts feel; and 2) it points toward a path of recovery.

An alcoholic's body must heal. His brain must heal. But his spirit must heal too. Whatever solution one finds for addiction, that solution must be powerful enough to overcome years of shame. It must help one reconcile the terrible sense that he has wasted his life. It must fill the void when recovery takes away from him what has provided structure, meaning, freedom, and fun. It must reverse cynicism. It must heal resentfulness.

Addiction's damage is total. It destroys faith. "Prove it" becomes the addict's attitude. It diminishes hope - hope that he can recover, hope that his family will ever trust him again. Addiction renders one unloved and unloving, unfit to give love, and unworthy to receive it. It creates despair even in those who have the things which should make life hopeful, such as a job, home, and loved ones. Relapse after relapse deadens the spirit. Skid row renders in visible terms what happens inside to many.

4

MORAL PROBLEM, SYMPTOM, OR DISEASE?

Calling alcoholism a disease seems a cop-out at first. Hard-liners are concerned that if alcoholism is called a "disease," drug addiction will be next. Then bad habits will be considered diseases. Finally the word "disease" itself will mean anything which is wrong with anyone. For sure, it is a crime against language when words become meaningless because they are used to refer to everything. But fear that every ache and pain, simple discomfort, or even the common cold will be classified as diseases should not keep reasonable people from considering alcoholism a "disease" if it fits or if "disease" explains the phenomenon.

The truth is that "disease" does a better job of explaining what happens to people who develop a drinking problem than any other name that has been used to label that process. "Disease" better explains the sheer number of alcoholics, millions of them in this country alone, than the notion that so many people would develop the same weakness or an identical form of sinfulness. "Disease" sheds more light on why such a wide range of personalities develop a drinking problem than does the notion that so many different types would have fallen victim to the very same personal failing. "Disease" is more logical than "psychiatric disorder" as a way to explain why many alcoholics recover without professional psychiatric treatment. That is, unless, we are prepared to accept the unlikely proposition that hundreds of thousands of psychiatrically disturbed people would have their serious psychiatric problems spontaneously remit, or in other words, just go away.

Some recovering alcoholics consider the controversy over whether alcoholism is a disease, an illness, a lifestyle inconvenience, or a simple misbehavior academic at best. To them, what is important is that they have it regardless of what it's called. Others, however, suffer unnecessarily because they hold on to notions they learned as children: that an alcoholic is a bum, a wastrel, or a misanthrope; that he is misguided, incorrigible, spineless, and weak; that he has a dependent, compulsive, incompetent, inadequate, or sociopathic personality; or that he is a sinner. Based on such thinking, they pursue a course aimed at reforming bad habits rather than doing the one thing which will help, namely, abstaining from alcohol.

Searching for a Name: In one sense, and without meaning to diminish it, the "degeneracy versus disease" debate is about a name. The issue is as much philosophical as it is medical. Therefore, it is important to consider what we expect of a name when we use it to label an experience.

We hang a name on a new experience hoping to accomplish two things. First, we hope the name sheds light on the new experience by pointing out how it is similar to something already familiar. We hope that when others come across the experience they will have a notion about what to expect because of the name. Second, we hope the name leaves nothing major unexplained. If we call a room which is the size of a telephone booth a "movie theater," that name fails to explain a great deal about the room. Specifically, that only one person at a time can watch a movie in it. The name is useless. Traditionally, alcoholism has been labeled a "moral problem," a "symptom of an underlying psychiatric disorder," and a "primary disease." Which does the best job?

Observations about Alcoholism: Most people have limited opportunity to observe alcoholism. A layman's observations are limited usually to just a few cases, and often those are cases with whom the observer is emotionally involved. Little is learned about alcoholism from such observations.

On the other hand, suppose one had the chance to witness thousands of cases representing a variety of people from different cultures in different social settings and at different periods in human history. Then suppose they had the chance to witness the life span of the affected individuals, and not just a slice of that life. Finally, suppose they got to see that history from a detached vantage point. Then, several characteristics would emerge. Whatever name we give alcoholism must shed light on a problem which is:

- insidious;
- complex;
- primary;
- chronic;
- progressive; and
- treatable.

An Insidious Problem: Chemical dependency is insidious. In other words, it's sneaky. It is sneaky in several ways. An alcoholic considers alcohol his friend not his enemy; a problem solver not a problem causer. Because they focus on immediate effects, alcoholics believe alcohol makes them feel good. Except for hangovers, and some do not suffer severe hangovers, alcoholics do not connect the unpleasant agitation they feel the following afternoon and evening to alcohol. On Friday he feels good, but the price he pays for Friday's pleasure lasts most of the following day. And as dependency grows, that price can last part of the next week as well.

Chemical dependency is sneaky in another way. Its damage is not always visible and not always dramatic. Health problems caused by alcohol abuse go undetected for a long time. To the world, many a functioning alcoholic appears a model parent, an outstanding citizen, and a hard worker. Even astute family members are embarrassed when they learn they have been living with an active alcoholic for years without realizing it.

The onset and progression of symptoms is another of addiction's insidious ways. In some cases, the problem develops so gradually that it is imperceptible. In other cases, symptoms appear so early that they are not considered "symptoms" at all. For someone whose drinking has been pathological from the start, it takes time to realize there is something unusual about that.

A Complex Problem: When alcoholism is called complex, what is meant is that it is a multi-faceted problem, not a single faceted one. And each of its facets, such as causes, effects, and peripheral results, are complex as well. Addiction is a complex of causative factors, a problem which gives birth to problems, and an illness that affects its victims in a variety of ways.

Complex Causes

"What causes compulsive drinking?" and "What causes alcoholism?" are related questions, yet different ones. Science will some day convince the world that the reason one person is prone to alcohol addiction and another not, has to do with the biochemical differences between them. In other words, heavy drinking or drug use; adaptation to a drug; growing compulsive use; craving; sensitivity to the damage a drug does; tolerance for it; or any combination of these factors, are matters primarily (if not exclusively) of one's biochemical make-up, not his personality. And yet it seems simplistic to conceive of an addiction which takes years to develop as the result of a single or even a cluster of biochemical factors alone. When it is defined as drinking which causes problems, alcoholism involves multiple forces. One such force (though a crucial one for sure) is one's biochemical pre-disposition toward compulsive alcohol use.

Until 1991, Alcoholics Anonymous World Headquarters compiled membership data from around the world. The country with the fewest A. A. groups per capita was Portugal with 0.6 groups per million people. Iceland was the highest with almost 800 groups per million, even though the Portuguese consume two and a half times as much alcohol per capita as Icelanders (Peele, 1997). In a study comparing percentage of abstainers and rates of alcohol dependence in Irish and Italian subjects, one study reports that even though there were a higher percentage of abstainers in the 76 Irish subjects, that group had seven times the rate of alcohol dependent subjects as a group of 99 Italians (Vaillant, 1983, p. 60).

By itself, alcohol no more causes alcoholism than gasoline causes automobile accidents. Alcohol is an ingredient and a necessary one, but the role it plays is analogous to the role of the baseball in a baseball game. The ball is essential to the game. One cannot play the game without it, but by itself (without players, bats, bases, umpires, and a field) the ball will not cause a baseball game. It will just sit on the pitcher's mound. Alcohols role in alcoholism is similar.

The making of bread provides an analogy for how multiple factors come together to create, in alcoholism's case, a problem. Bread is the result of several ingredients. The first ingredient, a "magic" ingredient, that might be called "susceptible" to becoming bread, is yeast. Yeast needs warm water to activate its potential, or else it will sit on the table being nothing more than yeast. Add flour, sugar, salt and other ingredients, and each loaf of bread gets a distinctive *character,* either French or Pumpernickel. Finally, the mixture needs time for rising and an oven for baking. Each of bread's ingredients has an analogue in alcoholism.

Yeast and Water – Susceptible Host and Activating Agent

Yeast has the potential to be bread. It might be called *prone or susceptible* to becoming bread. In alcoholism what is the analog to yeast? Research has yet to identify exactly which factor or factors make one prone to alcoholism, but research from different sources points to genetic factors (Bohman, 1978; Bohman, Sigvardsson, & Cloninger, 1981; Cadoret, Cain, & Grove, 1980; Goodwin, 1976 and 1979; Goodwin, Schulsinger, Hermansen, Guze, & Winokur, 1973; Goodwin, Schulsinger, Moller, Hermansen, Winokur, & Guze, 1974; Schuckit, 1980; Schuckit, Goodwin, & Winokur, 1972; Schuckit & Rayses, 1979). Some research even suggests that the reason one person may prefer stimulant drugs, and another depressants, is because of mechanisms under neurogenetic, not psychological, control (Cloninger, 1987). Adaptation, tolerance, and *loss of control*, which are so characteristic of alcoholic drinking, may be the products of genetic factors (Milam & Ketcham, 1981, p. 32). In other words, research suggests not that alcoholism is inherited, but that susceptibility to it may be passed on genetically.

Actually one does not have to read detailed research to believe that susceptibility to mood altering drugs, such as alcohol, is a biochemical matter. Concerning other drugs, such as analgesics, antibiotics, and anti-hypertensives, most people readily accept that in any group of people there is likely to be a percentage who will respond to a particular drug in a troublesome way. Aspirin, for example, provides quick and effective relief for some headache sufferers, while others need double doses to get the relief. Some few find that aspirin so irritates the stomach they rarely use aspirin. Antibiotics work wonders for most people. But some get a rash, and others have difficulty breathing when they take antibiotics. Like aspirin and penicillin, alcohol is a drug. And so, what is true for one drug, like Ibuprofen, is likely to prove true for another, like gin. Quite simply, there will always be people who are resistant to the effects of a drug, those who are susceptible to having problems because of them, as well as those for whom the drug is effective and safe.

Claiming that genetic factors are involved in developing a drinking problem is not to say that everyone who has an alcoholic parent is doomed to become an alcoholic. What it says is that alcoholism is a disease that involves a "susceptible host," one in whom a kind of yeast waits to be activated. But before yeast becomes bread it must meet water. Water kicks off yeast's potential; it is an activating "agent." Alcoholism's agent is alcohol, an activator and stimulator which starts a process and nourishes it along. When defined as "drinking which causes problems," alcoholism is impossible without alcohol. Infants are not born already divorced, fired from jobs, or charged with driving while intoxicated. An infant may be born susceptible to alcohol, a potential alcoholic; but if he never drinks, he will never know.

Character Factors

Yeast and water are not bread; you can't spread butter on that mix. Other ingredients must be added, such as flour, salt, and sugar. These ingredients give each loaf of bread its texture, substance, and flavor; its distinctive *character* so to speak.

When it comes to chemical dependency, these ingredients are personality and character. Psychological factors do play a role in alcoholism, but the factors that play a role are not always pathological or abnormal. In fact, any turn of mind which supplies a susceptible drinker with a reason to drink plays a role in feeding his susceptibility. It is to be expected, therefore, that the behavioral factors involved in a developing addiction will differ with individuals. One person's reason for drinking may be as innocent as his belief that alcohol is the way to celebrate. And he celebrates regularly. Someone whose life is stressful and who turns to alcohol in times of stress will find stress playing a role in his developing an addiction; provided that he finds the benefit alcohol offers comes without serious penalty. A thrill seeker is at greater risk for cocaine use than someone temperamentally conservative, if of course, the thrill seeker loves the drug high. Someone with an anxiety disorder will find anxiety plays a role provided he is tolerant of drugs or susceptible to their pleasures. Even an Irish mind-set about the remarkable qualities of alcohol can play a role as it most certainly has. A fun lover may drink too, provided he likes the fun alcohol provides and does not suffer greatly to pay for that fun. Exposure itself doesn't cause a drinking problem. What exposure might do is reveal the extent to which a drinker is either susceptible to drinking more or protected against it. Some people are protected from alcohol's damaging effects for a lifetime. Others are not.

What gets addiction started is one thing. What keeps it going is quite another. People take their very first drink for a variety of reasons. Alcoholics, however, take the thousandth drink because alcoholism begins supplying new reasons and new changes in brain systems along the way. It supplies new stresses and creates new pressures to justify drug use and to continue it. When addiction cannot find a ready-made excuse, it invents one.

At some point, addiction self-perpetuates, creating whatever it needs to continue, and even creating the very stuff on which it feeds. These factors are likely to be complex; the result of biochemical factors, growing physical dependence and complex psychological and environmental factors as well. Eventually, addiction creates both the chemistry and the psychology it needs to survive. The wife concerned that she may be driving her husband to drink need not be concerned. Addiction supplies all the drivers it needs.

The Role of Denial

In order to become an alcoholic, one psychological factor must enter the picture. That factor is denial. Quite simply, in order for drinking to continue causing problems, one must deny that it is causing them. The drinker who recognizes that drinking is a problem will do something about it. In denial, an addicted drinker doesn't recognize that, and so he continues. Denial is an essential ingredient.

Denial: Normal and Useful

To think that the mere presence of denial proves that an alcoholic is psychologically unstable, however, is a mistake. Defense mechanisms are not pathology. They become problematic when they backfire. A woman who knits as a way of dealing with her fear of flying uses a helpful and healthy defense. And she gets to her destination with a scarf in the bargain. If she is still knitting as she gets off the plane, trips and stabs herself with the knitting needle, knitting becomes a problem.

Denial of what is painful and unpleasant is part of the coping repertoire of all human beings. At times, denial is a blessing making it possible for a person to function throughout a traumatic event such as a disaster. For a while, denial helps families deal with the viewing, funeral service, and burial of a loved one. Later, when family members are better able to handle it, the reality of the loss hits. Denial makes it possible for passengers to board roller coasters and airplanes. Denial helps soldiers face battle. Denial helps mothers face childbirth, especially the births of second and third children. Denial had to play a part when the forty-one year old Columbus set sail from Spain in the 1492, and five hundred years later it must have helped Armstrong, Aldrin and Collins set sail for the moon. Denial helps love become marriage, making it possible for lovers to overlook the flaws in each other. And if it plays no role in first marriages, consider the role it plays in second marriages or third. Airline passengers, soldiers, mothers, explorers and lovers are not considered in psychological ill health generally. The unfortunate fact is that addicts are lovers. They love their drug. They love the zone the drug puts them in. They are not likely to find fault with it.

An addict's denial may center on nothing more than his drinking and drugging. In other respects, he may be a model of how to face reality and deal with it. When it comes to drinking, however, he is defensive and full of rationalizations. Once started, denial becomes integral to the three-pronged process in which drinking, problems, and denial form a circle.

Alcoholism's Oven

Alcoholism's final ingredients are analogous to those elements involved in bread's rising and baking. That is, a time and a place. That environment plays a role in alcoholism does not mean that certain places and certain cities cause alcoholism, or that certain jobs cause it. They clearly do not. Family members, companions, and friends do not cause alcoholism. Neither do cultures, societies, and neighborhoods. Each of these "places," however, can play a role in the process. For instance, a potential alcoholic who grows up in a world in which drinking is part of the regular after-work ritual will find that such a world provides opportunities for everyone to drink on a regular basis, including those susceptible to alcoholism.

Jobs do not cause addiction, but if a job either permits or encourages drinking with clients, then the job plays a role. Family stress does not make a person drink, but it may well provide a budding alcoholic an excuse to drink, and at the same time, someone to blame it on. Ovens do not cause bread. They provide an ideal place for it to bake.

If you take a seed, put it in fertile soil in a sunny location, and water it, that seed has a chance of becoming a flower. If you take a susceptible host, surround him with enablers, and give him a drink and a denial system, then there is a chance you might find yourself growing a problem drinker.

A Complex Problem

Alcoholism is not just a set of complex causes. Its impact is complex as well. Addicts get sick mentally, emotionally, physically, and even spiritually. Livers swell. Egos swell. Thinking contorts. Feelings distort. Given time, alcoholism takes a susceptible host and turns him into a bitter, cynical, hopeless, mistrustful, unloving, and dispirited drunk. No part of a human being is left untouched. Few other problems do as thorough a job.

Complex Effects

The keeper of a small town jail was asked how many inmates occupied cells in his jail because due to alcohol and drug abuse. He answered that if he freed the drug and alcohol cases, he could lock the rest in the bathroom (his was a more colorful word). If nothing else, addiction makes for trouble.

Alcoholism creates all sorts of problems. It disrupts families. It creates disturbances in neighborhoods. It is a civic and a courtroom problem. It is a headache for legislators and police. It is a national health problem. It costs business and industry billions of dollars through waste and damage, thus raising the costs of production and insurance. It scars children who live with it; scars which remain unhealed well after they have grown up. Addiction is a problem for schools. Addiction appears to be on the way to becoming the Pandora's Box of the Twenty First Century.

A Primary Problem: In Medicine, "primary" is a word used
with two distinct meanings. First, "primary" indicates which of several problems has caused a patient to be hospitalized, and which problem is, therefore, the focus of his treatment. Second, "primary" indicates whether a disease has its own cause (is "primary"), or is caused by another disease (is "secondary"). The question of whether alcoholism is a disease or a symptom of a disease is essentially a question of whether it is primary or secondary. Those who hold that drinking is symptomatic of a psychiatric disorder believe that it is secondary, not primary. It begs the question, therefore, to assume that alcoholism is primary in order to prove it is a disease.

Anyone who has visited a hospital emergency room at 2:00 a.m. on a Sunday morning has seen people who had been functioning the preceding afternoon rendered dysfunctional within hours because of their drinking. From that experience, one can easily conclude that drinking is a primary disorder in the first sense of the word. But is it primary in the second sense? It is the purpose of this entire chapter to demonstrate that chemical dependency is a primary disease. At this point, however, one thought might tease us into wondering whether alcoholism has its roots in immorality or insanity. Individual psychiatrists and priests have helped alcoholics recover, but in general, psychiatry and religion have had little success dealing with alcoholism. Instead, alcoholics have gotten well from the advice they get from each other. The only group with a track record for recovery is a group of people who have no training in morality or mental health, who would not recognize an "id" from a "superego" if they tripped over them, and who have no expertise in human dynamics and spiritual counseling. But this group has no equal when it comes to abstaining from alcohol and being happy at the same time. Alcoholics Anonymous has the track record for recovery.

The fact that Alcoholics Anonymous has been effective, does not establish alcoholism as a disease. What it demonstrates is that treatment administered by professionals is not essential to recovery for everyone. This is not to say that treatment is unimportant. Where denial is adamant, treatment is critical. Where hope is dim, treatment is life saving. And when addiction is complicated by a psychiatric illness, expert treatment is necessary. One of the ironies of addiction may prove to be that the earlier it is detected, the more we may need people who are specially trained to deal with the denial which accompanies it.

A Drunking Problem

The hypothesis that drinking is a symptom of a psychiatric illness rests on the assumption that the alcoholic's primary problem is psychiatric and his drinking is secondary. The thinking goes like this. An addict's problem has to do with his reason or reasons for turning to alcohol and/or other drugs. His drinking both reveals that he has problems, while at the same time, drinking conceals what those problems might be. The goal of treatment is to uncover and resolve an alcoholic's underlying need to drink. Once therapy succeeds and the underlying psychic turmoil resolved, drinking will no longer be a problem. Drinking, in other words, is not the alcoholic's real problem.

The assumption is half true. An alcoholic does not have a "drinking" problem. He has a "drunking" problem. Exploring why he drinks may intrigue the explorer, but whatever the reason, it is irrelevant to the specific problem an alcoholic has with alcohol. That problem concerns not his startings; it concerns his persistent failure at its stoppings. *Loss of control*, what happens *after* he starts, is at the heart of the alcoholic's problem. For some time, Alcoholics Anonymous has captured this core truth in a single sentence. "It's the first drink that gets you drunk."

Some alcoholics understand all too well *the reasons* they drink. They failed in business, or they succeeded at it. They are lonely. They are happy. They are angry. They are depressed. They feel nothing. Family life is boring. They wanted to have fun. The job is stressful. They want out of a loveless marriage. They love to celebrate. They want to escape. They resent their parents. They resent their coach. They resent the American Economic System. They got promoted; or they didn't. They live in an unhappy home. They have been cheated by life. They won. They lost. They didn't get a chance to play. Insight, however, does not solve a drunking problem. Once sober, knowing why he drinks may help an alcoholic avoid the first drink and, thereby, avoid the process. But even with the aid of an understanding psychotherapist, the alcoholic who gains insight into his motivation, the quirks of his personality and the dynamics which shaped his early childhood, is still unable to drink without losing control. In other words, he cannot drink without drunking. It is not always motivation that baffles alcoholics. What baffles them is that they end up drunk both when they want to and when they don't. And so, the question, "Why does he drink?" misses the point. The pertinent question is "Why does he drunk?"

Properly understood, alcoholism is A Drunking Problem.

A Chronic Disorder: Alcoholism is a chronic disorder; it doesn't go away. Like other diseases, diabetes for example, alcoholism is not cured. Alcoholism is arrested. Sober A. A. members refer to themselves as "recovering" rather than "recovered" to avoid suggesting that their inability to handle alcohol disappears when they are abstinent. Though an abstinent alcoholic will not suffer symptoms as long as he remains abstinent, his condition doesn't go away. He is never cured of his susceptibility. Recovery is a process and not an end point.

Not all professionals have accepted alcoholism's chronic nature. Some have maintained that alcoholics can be retrained to be social drinkers (Sobell & Sobell, 1973, 1976, and 1978), and that an alcoholic's compulsive drinking is reversible. Others (Pendery, Maltzman & West, 1982) have refuted that claim. In a re-investigation of twenty alcoholics reported in an earlier study (Sobell & Sobell, 1973, 1976, and 1978) as having mastered the return to controlled drinking, researchers found that except for one in a group of twenty, none of the remaining nineteen had been successful at returning to problem-free drinking as the earlier study had reported. Eight of the subjects continued to drink excessively with alcohol-related consequences. Six abandoned their attempts at controlled drinking and opted for abstinence as their treatment. One could not be found. Four had died alcohol-related deaths. Not a single dependent subject had become a successful controlled social drinker (Pendery et al., 1982).

A Progressive Disorder: Nearly every addiction counselor
                                               has seen, first hand, several cases
like the following. A woman was hospitalized for the first time at the
end of a twenty-four year drinking history and remained abstinent
for twelve years. She then resumed drinking. Within one year, she
was hospitalized four times, twice to be detoxified and twice for rehabilitation. Drinkers who have developed tolerance and who have
experienced a pattern of *loss of control* consistently report that when
they drank after a period of abstinence, their drinking and its symptoms picked up not where they left off, but at a worse stage. This
suggests that even during abstinence, addiction's processes progress
unseen. Addiction gets worse in one or all of the following ways:

- The amount and/or frequency of drug use increases.
- The problems caused become more intense and/or more
  frequent.
- Personality distorts in increasingly troublesome ways.

Though quite often an alcoholic's drinking gets worse (increasing frequency and in greater amounts), sometimes it is not drinking,
but the problems caused by drinking, that get worse. An individual
convicted of a single count of driving while intoxicated (DWI) in the
first ten drinking years of his drinking later collects three DWIs in a
single year. What used to be "marital discord" becomes "divorce."
"Problems at work" turn into "dismissals." Perhaps the most destructive way in which chemical dependency progresses is in the
way it distorts personality. A patient who had been drinking a fifth
of whiskey every day for several years was admitted to a hospital
and detoxified. In short order his sense of humor returned. He was
charming. A year later he relapsed, stayed drunk for six months and
was readmitted to the same hospital. This time, he was drinking a
"mere" pint a day. After his second detoxification, however, he was
cynical, bitter and resentful. Wrecked lives, as well as wrecked livers, destroy alcoholics.

If chemical dependency is insidious, complex, chronic, and progressive, which name best accounts for it?

Moral Problem? Those who call chemical dependency a moral problem believe addicts suffer from a sinful disposition, a persistent bad habit, an absence of moral fiber, a lack of values, inadequate upbringing, a weak will, and/or a defect in character. Excessive drinking, they believe, is either a sin, or at the very least, a nuisance. According to proponents of this hypothesis, an alcoholic has a malicious, misguided, or defective will. His problem is will power, or rather, his lack of it. In short, they believe addicts are weak or bad, or both, and so the aim of treatment is to make them strong or good, or both.

Only within the past fifty years has alcoholism been considered a disease by other than isolated clusters of people. Even today, generally open-minded people react with disbelief when addiction is called a "disease" because it looks like no other disease they have seen before. Others are not so generous, and some are downright angry. Having been subjected to cruel, abusive, destructive, outrageous, bizarre and criminal behavior, they want alcoholics punished not coddled. To them, calling alcoholism a disease seems just another way of letting alcoholics off the hook. Angry proponents of the Moral Problem hypothesis feel that they can explain their anger more easily if they see themselves as angry at a bad person rather than at a sick one. Thus the notion that addiction is a moral problem is an appealing one.

Exposure Implies Intention?

Those who support the notion that addiction is a moral problem offer several reasons for this belief. They argue that anyone who takes a risk is to blame for whatever results from the risk. This sentiment is expressed in the words "he brought it on himself" or "he has no one to blame but himself." The implications are interesting. The first is one with which few would disagree, namely that whoever takes a risk is responsible for dealing with its consequences. If while driving my car I have an accident, I am responsible for repairing the damage as no one else will. The second implication, however, is subtle and illogical. If a disaster does result from my taking a risk, does that necessarily mean that I was at fault or "to blame" for the disaster?

To be "responsible for" and to be "blame for" are not synonymous and interchangeable words. Every time I drive a car, I risk having an accident whether I drive recklessly or not. If I have an accident, no one will take my car to the repair shop except me. But because I am responsible for handling the consequences, does not mean I intended those consequences, or that I am "to blame" for them. When I wade into an ocean, I risk drowning. Would it follow that if I did drown, that I was "to blame" for it? Driven to its logical conclusion, this sort of reasoning would hold that people who eat red meat want to have heart attacks, that Father Damian meant to contract leprosy, and that physicians who treat AIDS patients are subconsciously suicidal.

An addict is responsible for treating his addiction, once he knows he has an addiction. The problem is that denial keeps him from knowing that he has one.

Solutions Reveal Causes?

Another reason for refusing to accept alcoholism as a disease is based on the presumption that addiction cannot be called a disease until its exact cause is known. Proponents further argue that since recovery involves neither pills, nor surgery, nor medical intervention, alcoholism may be a problem. But it is not rightly a disease.

This is a variation on the notion that solutions to problems point to their causes. In other words, a problem which is solved by an act of will power (the "will" to remain sober) must have been caused by the absence of will power, and therefore, not a disease.

The truth is, however, that solutions do not point to their causes all the time. Antibiotics cure infection; their absence does not cause infection. Some diabetics recover without medication if they conform to a diet; their treatment is an act of will. The fact that will power solves this type of diabetes does not mean that lack of will power caused diabetes in the first place. Alcoholics Anonymous found a solution that is spiritual, but that does not mean that alcoholic drinking is a sin. What A. A. understood from the start is that having lost a powerful means of altering one's mood, and having given up something he loves, a recovering alcoholic may need an equally powerful replacement.

Only Bad People Do Bad Things?

When people believe that alcoholism is a moral problem, they believe so, in part, because they reason that since drunks do bad things, they must be bad people. Thus, alcoholism is an expression of badness and not a disease. There is a simpler explanation. An alcoholic is drugged. His behavior is directed by a drug-sedated and drug-irritated brain. Drugged-conceived behavior is then expressed without the benefit of a clear brain's censoring, regulating, and inhibiting functions. Such behavior is bound to be distorted. The dogged persistence that alcohol is truth serum still prompts people to believe that what a person does under its influence reveals the type of person he is. The truth is that alcohol distorts and/or exaggerates who or what someone is.

Few non-alcoholics want their personalities analyzed based on what they have said or done in a hospital recovery room after surgery and under sedation. Under such conditions, people say and do all sorts of crazy things, which are uncharacteristic and atypical of their usual behavior. To analyze someone who is drunk in his living room is to analyze him on similar grounds. And to believe that because *some* alcoholics do bad things that *all* alcoholics have a moral problem is a leap of several dimensions. Very little can be said of his moral character when an alcoholic is drunk, except that his behavior is drug-conceived, drug-directed, drug-exaggerated, drug-distorted, drug-expressed, and lacking the benefit of the brain's censoring function.

Drinking is Voluntary?

There is another, and at first glance more compelling, reason for presuming alcoholism a moral problem. Drinking appears to be a totally voluntary act, and thus drug addiction is thought to be self-inflicted. On the surface, it seems that alcoholics make themselves alcoholics by drinking too much. The conclusion is based on two suppositions. The first is that since *some* people do, in fact, control their drinking, that *all* people must be able to control it. The second is that since drinking *seems* completely voluntary, that it *is* completely voluntary, or solely an act of will. Those who accept these assumptions interpret excessive drinking as indicating an incorrect, defective, spiteful or malicious will. A few who take this position acknowledge that alcoholism eventually does become a disease. However, they believe it was a disease caused by irresponsibility, weakness, or poor judgment in the first place.

Drinking *Appears* Voluntary

No drug has an identical effect on everyone who uses it. Some people find a drug works wonderfully well, even at a low dose. Others take the same dose, and it doesn't work at all. Some people get sick when they take the very same drug. There is simply no universal single response to drugs. And because alcohol, cocaine, and heroin are drugs, human beings are likely to respond to those drugs in a variety of ways. Forces other than will power govern those ways. It is not the human will which is in complete control and regulates how one responds to a drug. His brain is involved too. Some people can't handle aspirin. Others can't handle Anisette.

If a robbery were videotaped without showing the robber holding the gun, it would appear that a distressed person was giving his money away. When the gun comes into view, the force which motivates the victim's behavior becomes apparent. Things are not always as they seem. Drinking *seems* voluntary, but the forces which drive it are not always visible.

There is clearly one instance in which the drinking of alcohol *appears* to be voluntary but is not. Withdrawal develops on a continuum. At some point withdrawal becomes measurable or "visible." Just the week before, however, the discomfort of withdrawal was bothersome but not visible. In such a condition, a drinker appears to choose alcohol, when actually he drinks to calm the jitters of a withdrawal which neither he nor anyone else is able to see. His drinking is an act of self-medication, not of will.

Acute and sub-acute withdrawal can explain why those who are already dependent on alcohol drink out of control. But why does someone who has yet to reach the withdrawal stage drink one after another in a relentless, seemingly compulsive way? Why do alcoholics drink too much before they are physically dependent, before they suffer any withdrawal at all? The anecdotal evidence gathered from numbers of recovering alcoholics is that they were prone to have trouble from the start, and that the drug took its hold quickly. Dr. Erickson notes in *The Science of Addiction* (2007, p. 60) "some 'addicts' report instant dependence." Dr. Erickson also suggests that any researcher trying to understand the processes of addiction must take into account that there are people who drink heavily and do not become chemically dependent or addicted. And there are also others, who do drink moderately, and yet they do lose control to an extent. They do develop craving. They do develop a strong desire for alcohol. They do grow tolerant for the drug. And they do persist in drinking despite a desire to stop or repeated problems because of it. They do, in fact, become addicted. Are some people prone to alcohol addiction from the start?

Research with Sons of Alcoholics

Many years ago, Dr. Marc Schuckit published research that demonstrates that sons of alcoholics, even before they are experienced drinkers, perceive, experience, and process alcohol differently than the sons of non-alcoholics (see Schuckit & Rayses, 1979; Schuckit, Engstrom, Alpert, & Duby, 1981; Schuckit, 1984b). The young men in Schuckit's studies could not have turned themselves into alcoholics because they had not been drinkers long enough to have changed their body's chemistry through drinking. In fact, if a subject's drinking was suspicious, he was eliminated from the study. Still the young men in these studies differ from their fellows in four ways:

- They are not as adept at judging the level of their intoxication.

- They build up more acetaldehyde (a potent toxin produced in the breakdown of alcohol), though not enough to cause an aversive Antabuse reaction.

- They experience a measurably greater degree of the release of muscle tension from drinking than do the sons of non-alcoholics.

- They exhibit less body sway when under the influence than do their family history negative cohorts.

In other words, they are not good at knowing how drunk they are. They pay a higher toxic price for drinking. They seem less affected by it. And they get a bigger kick from alcohol than do their peers. Little wonder why ten years down the line they are the ones in a crowd who will say, "One more and I'll go home," and then have six more.

The Alcoholic's Non-Reaction

Another reason certain individuals do drink too much is that they can. No inner mechanism helps them stop. Social drinkers do have an inner mechanism which helps them cut off after a couple drinks. Even when they try to keep pace with alcoholics drink for drink, social drinkers get sicker quicker. And they realize this. The wife of an alcoholic made a valiant effort to drink with her husband in order to keep him company but found she got sick trying. A husband tried to keep pace with his high tolerance alcoholic wife but found that he was the one who had to be carried home. Though they can ignore it, social drinkers have a built-in, early warning system about alcohol. One drink makes them feel good, and a second better. But if their blood alcohol level rises much further, a social drinker starts to feel, dizzy, groggy, sleepy, sick or unpleasantly out of control. These protective signals warn him that alcohol is a poison; it is not good for him. If he stops because of these warnings, it is hardly an act of pure self-control. His will does the smart thing; it cooperates with bodily warnings. Social drinkers can choose to drink beyond this point, but they would need a very strong desire to do so. Their chemistry rebels against it.

Unlike social drinkers, alcoholics report no such warnings. Or if they had such warnings at one time, that shut off valve broke. To them the first drink feels good; the second better; the third marvelous; the fourth outstanding; the fifth spectacular; and with the sixth drink they are on top of the world. They have no rheostat, no bodily rebellion, against increasing doses of poison until they have reached levels that would stun elephants. Without a shut off system, an alcoholic never finds it easy to stay within reasonable limits. And as long as some booze feels good and more feels better, he will always find it difficult to avoid drinking a lot.

Alcoholics have problems not only when they drink too much, they have trouble when they drink too little. In *Under the Influence,* Dr. James Milam points out that addiction reaches a point in which it is not his continuing to drink but stopping which causes an alcoholic an unpleasant feeling and a decrease in performance. At the bar, while imbibing, he is fine. On the way home his blood alcohol falls, and he starts to feel "out of it," and this experience is what impels another drink when he gets home. Though it appears he drinks because he wants to, the truth is he drinks partly to prevent from slipping into the dysfunction caused by too little alcohol in a system accustomed to more (Milam & Ketcham, 1981, pp. 52-53).

Anyone who is a poor judge of his intoxication, who has no rheostat to help limit his drinking, who gets a bigger boost from drinking than others, and who finds that a falling blood alcohol level feels worse than a rising one is likely to have problems controlling how much he drinks.

Future research is likely to provide additional explanations for why some people drink more than others as appears to be the direction of recent research (cf. Erickson, 2007). In the meantime, to assume that excessive alcohol and other drug use is an act regulated solely by the power of the will, uninfluenced by one's bodily response to drugs, begs several questions. The key questions are these:

- Is one's response to a psychoactive drug completely within the domain of the human mind?

- Do forces other than will power govern why some people may continue to use a drug repeatedly?

- Is it the brain or the mind that explains why some very good people persist in drug taking even after drug taking has caused problems?

It is cheating to argue that drug use is completely voluntary in order to prove that alcoholism is self-inflicted.

Even a few recovering addicts hold themselves responsible for causing their addictions, saying that they "chose to drink" or "chose to use drugs." The truth is that they chose alcohol not alcoholism. They chose drugs not drug addiction.

What "Moral Problem" Fails to Explain

Proclaiming addiction a moral problem sheds more light on the attitude of the proclaimer than it does about observations of the people who have gotten sick. It may be comforting to think that good people will not become addicted because they are good, but the fact is that a wide range of different folks, some very good people, in fact, do become alcoholic. Any group of alcoholics is made up of people from so many walks of life with such varied backgrounds, philosophies and upbringings that calling them all weak or bad stretches credibility. There are alcoholic priests. There are alcoholic prostitutes. "Moral problem" fails to explain the variety of its cases.

Moral problem fails to explain why training of the will, psychotherapy, religious conversion and moral rehabilitation fail to reverse an alcoholic's tolerance and impaired control. Calling alcoholism a moral problem fails to explain why someone who has passed the most strenuous test a society has ever devised for determining integrity, stamina, determination and will power (in other words, someone with the "right stuff" to be an astronaut) will fail to have enough self discipline to control his drinking.

To accept alcoholism as a moral problem requires embracing a whopping set of assumptions. One must first believe that ten to eighteen million people in the United States have developed an identical moral problem. One must also accept that the moral failing these millions have developed will manifest in the same way in all of them, namely, by inability to handle alcohol. Furthermore, one must accept that this particular moral failing will take the same form for athletes and weaklings, bums and businessmen, con men and congressmen (is there a difference?), free loaders and First Ladies alike. To continue to believe that alcoholism is a moral problem requires that one accept that those alcoholics who have demonstrated remarkable self-control in the other areas of their lives would suddenly exhibit a selective loss of control in a single area.

If alcoholism is a weak person's response to stress, why does it not occur at similar rates among people who have suffered similar stresses? American Indians have had a fair share of stress with high rates of alcoholism, but as a group, Jews have had as much stress but with a significantly lower rate of alcoholism (Milam & Ketcham, 1981, pp. 40-41).

To call alcoholism a disease does not mean that every alcoholic is innocent. Some alcoholics are nasty, incompetent, and anti-social, whether drunk or sober. To call alcoholism a disease does not mean that behavior plays no role in addiction. A drinking problem is impossible without two behaviors, drinking and denying. What calling alcoholism a disease means is that one need not be immoral, weak, or pathologically sick. Even moral and psychologically ordinary people become addicts.

Symptom of an Underlying Disorder? Symptom, a secondary manifestation of an underlying psychiatric disorder, is another name given to alcoholism. Alcoholism can mimic nearly any psychiatric problem. Because there are alcoholics who exhibit only psychological symptoms (health symptoms and social consequences are minimal or go undetected), it is a small step to conclude that if, on the surface, a problem *looks* psychological, then underneath there must be a psychological problem.

Those who believe the "symptom" hypothesis hold that abusive drinking is caused by unresolved psychic conflict or serious psychiatric illness, and that mental-emotional problems are obscured beneath a cloud of alcohol and special treatment needed to resolve them. There are two variations on the hypothesis. One holds that an alcoholic's psychiatric problems cause him to become physically dependent on alcohol. Thus, he can never drink safely again, even after his psychiatric problems are resolved. The other holds that once an alcoholic's underlying problems are solved he will drink normally because he will no longer "need" to abuse alcohol or use other drugs excessively. In both versions, however, specialists with years of education about how to access unconscious psychic material and hidden motivation find it too simple to interpret a drinking problem as a problem with drinking.

Even some A. A. members believe alcoholism is a symptom and cite a couple of sentences from the book, *Alcoholics Anonymous* as what appears undeniable support for that belief. The "Big Book" says, "Our liquor was but a symptom. So we had to get down to causes and conditions" (AA, 1976, p. 64). Taken out of context the statement appears to say that alcoholism is a manifestation of another problem, that it is secondary. The context, in which that sentence appears, however, does not concern what causes alcoholism. The context concerns the barriers to overcoming alcoholism, not the pathology behind it. *"Getting down to causes,"* in other words, appears in a discussion of the defects of character which block spiritual recovery as that recovery is defined by a spiritual third step ("Made a decision to turn our will and our lives over to the care of God *as we understood Him*"). At this point the "Big Book" is not trying to explain why an alcoholic is compelled to drink. Rather it is elaborating the defects of character, specifically self centeredness, which get in the way of his recovery and of turning his will over to a "Higher Power." An *in-context* paraphrase of this section of *Alcoholics Anonymous* might sound something like this: *"Drinking was but one layer of the multiple layers of problems our alcoholic drinking fostered in us. At a deeper level, the self centeredness which our alcoholism nourished in us is what keeps us alcoholics from gaining and maintaining a contact with a Higher Power."* There is no reason to believe that the writer of the sentence, "Our drinking was but a symptom," was a psychiatrist speaking literally. Rather, the writer may well have been a stock broker speaking metaphorically about "symptoms." The fact is that from the beginning, the purpose of the "Big Book" has never been to provide a treatise on why people become alcoholic in the first place, but to show alcoholics how others have recovered (see the Foreword to the First Edition of *Alcoholics Anonymous*).

At first glance, "psychiatric disorder" does appear to account for a drinker's behavior. Alcoholics act crazy when they are drunk. Some act a little "off" on the days in between. They can be labile and unpredictable, full of nervous energy one moment and sullen the next. They sulk and brood. In three days they go from depressed to angry to suicidal. They do not look well glued together. And the reason is that they are not well glued together.

"Does an alcoholic look crazy?"

"Yes."

"Why does he look crazy?"

"He *looks* crazy because he *is crazy*."

The next question is the important one.

"Why is he crazy?"

"He is crazy from alcohol. And when he is not crazy *from* it, he is crazy *for* it."

An alcoholic suffers from an illness which involves multiple forces at work on him all at the same time. These forces can and do make alcoholics look crazy. A drug poisons his brain and distorts his perception. Denial affects his mind. His pursuit of the drug distorts his motivation. His feelings are blunted or exaggerated.

How can an alcoholic's "crazy" behavior be explained? Ockham's razor is the principle of reasoning which holds that when there are two ways to explain what causes a problem (the one a simple, obvious and straightforward explanation, and the other remote and complicated), one should go with the obvious and immediate explanation as the true explanation until proven otherwise. Using Ockham's razor, alcoholic drinking by itself can account for impulsive behavior, irrational behavior, indecisive behavior, persistent anger and resentment, rage, violence, fear, paranoia, anxiety, phobia, mistrust, mood lability, depression, agitation, flat and/or inappropriate affect, memory lapses, outbursts of physical and emotional fury, extreme thinking, vacillation, hypersensitivity, self-centeredness, egocentric thinking, immature responses to rejection, and a sense of entitlement. Less common, but still attributable to alcohol and other drugs are hallucinations, delusions, and other breaks from reality. As the result of acute intoxication, idiosyncratic intoxication, long term toxicity, and withdrawal, alcoholism is very much what LeClair Bissel, past president of the American Medical Society on Alcoholism, calls "the great masquerader" (Drews, 1983, p. 134).

An elegantly simple cut of Ockham's razor maintains that since alcohol can cause a drinker's symptoms, it should be thought that it does cause them. The only way to find out is to take alcohol away and see what happens. Many an alcoholic with what appeared to be troubling psychiatric symptoms during active addiction find those symptoms disappear with abstinent treatment. Some, of course, have psychiatric problems in addition to alcoholism, but those problems can be seen more clearly and treated more successfully after the bloat of alcoholism subsides.

There is one warning here. Simply to take alcohol away from an alcoholic is not to treat his alcoholism. Treatment involves more than abstinence, and yet what it does involve is specific to treating addiction. There is no lonelier, sadder, more resentful creature in the world than an alcoholic without booze. To treat addiction in a total way involves treating the resentments that have been part of the disease along with the loneliness that accompanies recovery from it. It involves treating the impact denial has had, years of it. Addiction treatment has to undo the impact of years of rationalizing. It includes learning how to have fun without drugs. It includes resolving "recovery's resentment" – the resentment at being alcoholic and having to treat the problem. Total recovery requires time to overcome guilt and shame. It requires that one reconcile to the loss of the drug and the lifestyle that accompanied it. An alcoholic who does nothing more than stop drinking is an untreated alcoholic. He is dry, not sober.

What "Symptom" Fails to Explain

For anyone who is drug tolerant, a discussion of whether addiction has physical or psychological origins is academic. The tolerant addicted drinker and drug user cannot use moderately. Either he drinks to excess to get the kick, or he may as well not drink at all. Few alcoholics, the number must be miniscule, deliberately work hard at developing tolerance, drinking and drugging until they get good at it. They do not train for it. Some were always tolerant, while others came to be tolerant with little effort on their part. To say that alcoholism's cause is psychogenic does not explain tolerance, especially cases of early high tolerance.

Claiming that addiction is a problem in which disturbed individuals act out serious psychiatric problems does not explain why, even after years of psychotherapy administered under abstinent conditions by addiction-trained psychiatrists, an alcoholic person still remains tolerant of alcohol. Nor does it explain why, if he resumes its use, he will return to even greater *loss of control* than before psychotherapy.

An intelligent woman who was about to be discharged from treatment insisted that she did not have alcoholism, but that she did have a psychiatric problem. Besides that, she didn't believe alcoholism was a disease. She was going to see a psychiatrist, and had no intention of going to A. A. A member of the staff had the presence of mind to recommend that if she were going to get psychiatric treatment, she should not pay a psychiatrist to work with someone who was drinking and alcohol affected. She should abstain during the period of her therapy. That made sense to her, so she followed the advice, remained abstinent, and worked in therapy for a couple of years. She was mentally healthier as a result. Regrettably, she decided to celebrate her new found mental health with a drink. Within six months she returned to treatment. Old-fashioned observation teaches us that addiction is progressive despite psychotherapy, solemn oaths, and even ordination to the priesthood.

Finally, proclaiming alcoholism a psychiatric disorder leaves unexplained how, since the founding of Alcoholics Anonymous, most have resumed healthy and productive lives without the help of mental health professionals.

Disease - Still Difficult to Accept: Despite both logic and evidence, it is still difficult to accept alcoholism as a disease. Americans who have been raised "to lift themselves up by their bootstraps" (an idiom which, incidentally, had to have been coined by someone who never wore boots) consider the solution to alcoholism so simple and so easy that it couldn't possibly be a disease. And even if it is a disease, it couldn't be a serious one.

Television viewers laugh at alcoholism, even advanced cases of it. In one situation comedy popular in the 1980s the show's funniest character is an itinerant preacher, turned taxi driver, who suffers significant brain damage because of alcohol and hallucinogens. It is difficult to laugh at this character (although we do), and at the same time view him as seriously and permanently brain damaged. Drunk and damaged alcoholics and addicts have for many years been members of the cast in American humor.

When hospitals offer wine as a beverage choice on a patient's lunch menu, it is difficult for the patient and his or her visitors to accept alcohol as a serious drug, and alcoholism a serious disease.

Addicts themselves find it difficult to accept disease as the explanation for addiction - but for different reasons. The addict who considers his problem a disease is sure to be terrified by it. Sooner or later even he will find it difficult to delude himself into thinking he can control a disease. Addicts like to think that their problem is a matter under their control. They want to believe that they simply haven't tried hard enough to control it thus far. Not really tried, that is.

Non-addicted family members have a hard time with the disease concept too. If they have suffered at the hands of an alcoholic, they are too angry to accept "disease" as explaining their experience. How could someone who is sick have caused them such rage? It is easier to believe that an alcoholic is bad, and that is why they are angry with him. For the family who does accept alcoholism as a disease, the future is no less frightening. Family members feel even less in control of a disease than they did when they thought the problem a will power issue. It is easier on the psyche to think that all an addict has to do is "get hold of himself."

A Definition of Disease: Definitions of disease are either so broad that any discomfort (even the common cold) qualifies, or so narrow that only one type of illness qualifies. A useful definition avoids extremes. Five elements make up a definition which is specific and flexible. A disease is:

- a destructive process
- in an organ or an organism
- with a specific cause or causative factors
- characteristic symptoms
- that get worse if untreated.

If chemical dependency is a disease, it will fit each of these criteria, and it does.

A Destructive Process

A disease is a destructive or disruptive process. Chemical dependency is a process. In fact, it is several processes. It is a process of adaptive tolerance and physical dependence (Milam & Ketcham, 1981). It is a history of morbidity (Vaillant, 1983). It is a progression of interactive, pathological family dynamics (Wegscheider, 1981). It is a string of intensifying symptoms (Jellinek, 1960).

Chemical dependency is destructive. When characterized by tolerance and loss of control, untreated alcoholism heads in the direction of jail, institutionalization, or death. In Maryland, Spring Grove is the name of a state mental hospital which was a domiciliary for chronically impaired, "wet brain" alcoholics. Baltimore A. A. members used to describe an active drinker's future as "the Group (A. A.), the Grove (Spring Grove), or the Grave."

Addiction's progression is predictable. Even though symptoms and their sequence vary with individuals, alcoholism progresses from early exposure. It starts with symptomatic use and progresses to loss of control, problematic use, compulsive drinking, and ending with serious morbidity. No one has that crystal ball which foresees recovery's course, but what happens to alcoholics who drink is predictable. It is this predictability, despite the variety of personalities who go through it, which provides persuasive testimony for chemical dependency as a disease rather than as a function of personality.

In an Organ or an Organism

Various sources and types of research postulate that alcoholics differ from non-alcoholics in bodily, not just psychological ways. These differences are not the consequence of drinking, but precede and cause it.

Genetic Markers

When they drink, the sons of alcoholics build up more acetaldehyde than their peers who have no family history of alcoholism (Korsten, Matsuzaki, Feinman, & Lieber, 1975). Some research demonstrates that individuals at high risk for alcoholism get more of a kick from drinking and are less able to know when they've had enough than others (Schuckit et. al., 1981; Schuckit, 1984b). Other research demonstrates that potential alcoholics pay a greater price than their low risk friends, getting sicker livers each time they drink (Lieber, 1976). Milam summarizes animal studies and other research which suggest that acetaldehyde interacts with other brain chemicals to form tetrahydroisoquinolines (THIQ), and that isoquinolines act on opiate receptors in the brain to explain the addictive qualities of alcohol (Milam & Ketcham, 1981, pp. 29-42). In one study, tetrahydropapaveroline, (produced when dopamine and acetaldehyde combine) was injected into the brains of rats who then chose alcohol over water and drank it until they developed withdrawal-like symptoms (Myers & Melchior, 1977).

One study of 262 male and female college students, ages 17 to 23, shows that students who carry two copies of the short version of a serotonin transporter gene are more likely to report troublesome drinking patterns. They engaged more frequently in binge drinking, drank more often to get drunk, and consumed more alcoholic drinks per occasion than students with the other genotypes. Another difference observed was that students with at least one copy of the long variant of 5HTT consumed a smaller number of drinks at a sitting, even though they went out to drink as often as the other students (Herman, Philbeck, Vasilopoulos, & DePetrello, 2003).

Brain Waves

Research into the differences between the brain waves of children of alcoholics and peers with no family alcoholism history suggests genetic factors are involved. A brain wave, called P-3, has been known to be deficient in chronic alcoholics. It was believed that alcoholics destroyed their P-3 capacity by drinking. Researchers, however, found differences between the P-3 voltage of boys with a family history and those who had no family history, even though the "high risk boys" were between 7 and 13 years old and had not consumed alcohol as part of the study (Begleiter, Porjesz, Bihari, & Kissin, 1984). Alpha waves are brain waves associated with states of well being. Sons of alcoholics, between 19 and 21 years old, who had not received an alcoholism diagnosis themselves, produced significantly more alpha waves from drinking than did a similar group of young men with no family history (Pollock, Volavka, Goodwin, Mednick, Gabrielli, Knop, & Schulsinger, 1983). Those prone to alcoholism may respond differently to alcohol from the outset.

Ethnic Susceptibility

Jews and Italians have lower rates of alcoholism than Native Americans (Milam & Ketcham, 1981). Koreans have an aversive response to alcohol. They respond to alcohol as if they had some sort of built-in Antabuse. This response has been called "The Asian Protection." A study of 24 Oriental subjects showed significantly more skin flushing, increased heart rate, drop in blood pressure, and general discomfort with alcohol than 24 Occidental subjects. In addition, the former more frequently reported family histories of skin flushing (Ewing, Rouse, & Pellezzari, 1974). A review of 17,500 arrest records in New York's Chinatown from 1933 to 1949 found that not one arrest noted public drunkenness (Barnett, 1955). Is it likely that the New York Chinese gained control over public drunkenness, or is it that drunkenness is not a major problem in Chinatown? It is generally recognized that Native Americans are more susceptible to alcohol problems, so that some reservations have made it illegal.

Animal Studies

Two animal studies focus attention on the dopamine system in interesting ways. The first demonstrates that gene therapy involving increasing levels of dopamine in rats accounts for a reduction of drinking in rats that have been trained to prefer alcohol (Thanos, Volkow, Freimuth, Umegaki, Hiroyuki, Roth, Ingram, & Hitzemann, 2001). The second, a follow up study, shows that gene therapy can reduce drinking even in rats with a genetic predisposition for heavy alcohol consumption (Thanos, Taintor, Rivera, Umegaki, Ikari, Roth, Ingram, Hitzemann, Fowler, Gatley, Wang, & Volkow, 2004). The irony of addiction might well be that a "mood altering" drug first robs the brain of its dopamine production by supplying dopamine, and then the drug becomes necessary to resupply the pleasure it has robbed.

Addiction is a complex disease involving dynamic brain, mind, and environmental factors and processes. The disease is progressive with changes occurring all along the way. The man or woman who begins the process is not the same person after several years. By the end, he or she may be virtually unrecognizable. For sure, any phenomenon that involves the twin complexities of the human brain and psychoactive drugs is not likely to be explained simply by a single factor.

The unlikely notion that addiction results from a single biochemical proneness factor is echoed by The Collaborative Study on the Genetics of Alcoholism (COGA), a large scale family study involving nine centers at universities across the United States. COGA has been designed not simply to demonstrate that genetic factors play a role in alcoholism, but to identify particular genes that affect that risk. Dr. Howard Edenberg of the Indiana University School of Medicine summarizes the design and current results in an update of the COGA Study. He acknowledges what COGA researchers have suspected. Namely, that "Multiple genes would contribute to the risk for alcoholism. In other words, there will be no single 'gene for alcoholism' but rather variations in many different genes that together, interacting with the environment, place some people at significantly higher risk for the disease." (Edenburg, 2003, par. 1).

Research continues. Though no single study nails a particular physiological peculiarity as *the* cause, the weight of research suggests that the tendency toward addiction, or protection against it, is more a matter of a complex sequence of brain processes (Koob & Bloom, 1988), involving the brain's dopamine system (Volkow, Wang, Begleiter, Porjesz, Fowler, Telang, Wong, Ma, Logan, Goldstein, Alexoff, & Thanos, 2006) (Erickson, 2007) than simply the result of an act or acts of the human will.   People who can't handle booze seem to have been born prone to that problem. Addiction involves more than can be explained by the way one's brain or liver handles a drug however. In order for a predilection to compulsive drug use to become full-fledged, and in order for cells to adapt to a drug, denial must enter the picture. Without denial, there is no progression! Without progression, there is no disease!

The simplest definition is that an alcoholic is a person with a brain that loves alcohol, a system that can't handle it, and a mind that keeps denying and trying.

Specific Causative Factors

Clearly, we do not have the definitive answer to alcoholism. Research into the other drug dependencies continues as well. However, one adoption study of 242 males and 201 females reports three correlates: 1) drug abuse correlates highly with antisocial personality which, in turn, was predicted from an antisocial biologic background; 2) a biologic background of alcohol problems predicts increased drug abuse even in adopted children who do not have antisocial personalities; and 3) environmental factors of divorce and psychiatric disturbance in the adoptive family are associated with drug abuse (Cadoret, Troughton, O'Gorman, & Heywood, 1986). There is also research that suggests that personality dimensions, such as "novelty seeking, harm avoidance and reward dependence" may reflect variations in brain systems which modulate behavioral responses to various classes of drugs (Cloninger, 1988, p. 66). Therefore, what seems one's preference for alcohol or cocaine may in actuality be influenced by underlying genetic mechanisms (Cloninger, 1988).

The evidence is mounting that the various drug addictions, including alcoholism, follow similar pathways. But research grows more difficult and complicated with each day. Few drug addicts today use a single drug. It is virtually impossible to find a pure marijuana addict, a pure cocaine addict, or a pure alcoholic. Thirty day inpatient treatment is increasingly rare. Today, the patient who is treated for more than six days is likely to be insured for addiction treatment as long as it co-exists with a psychiatric disorder. All of this further complicates the task of finding uncomplicated cases of the impact of particular drugs of abuse on particular individuals.

Going on faith may not satisfy those who insist that a problem is not legitimately classified a disease until its cause or causes are known. Such a position, followed to its logical conclusion, however, would prevent medicine from treating certain cancers and schizophrenia. The fact is that physicians successfully treat diseases for which we have only clues about causes. Alcoholism has been treated with success for many years even when we had no idea at all what caused it.

Characteristic Symptoms

Alcoholism produces characteristic symptoms, two of which deserve special attention because they are progressive and because a dynamic interaction exists between them: denial and loss of control.

Denial is that mechanism by which the mind defends itself against a reality too painful to tolerate. *Loss of control* describes the phenomenon in which a first drink, snort, or dose sets off a string of doses which leads to unintended intoxication and unpredictable behavior. Denial and *loss of control* work in tandem. An alcoholic loses control and denies it. Instead of seeing impaired control as the reason for his getting sick or drunk, he blames it on stress, family problems, the price of a good time, bad clams, shrimp, crabs or lobster (shell fish take more than their fair share of the blame for alcoholic vomiting), too much or too little to eat, mixing drinks, a disappointment in business, rejected love, or a death in the family. Instead of being alarmed by his lack of control, he explains it away.

When *loss of control* couples with its denial, alcoholism is set on a progressive course. From that point, an addicted person is not likely to see that he has a problem until it causes so much pain and trouble that even he can't avoid considering his inability to control alcohol the reason for his "drunking." For the process to end, forces outside the drinker must intervene. Addictive drinking and drugging is compulsive, plain and simple. Some never accept that. Some never see it.

Summary: If "disease" is a condition in which a bodily susceptibility (an "X" or proneness factor or factors), coupled with behavior (drinking and denial of problems related to it), leads to morbidity (sickness and problems), despite an individual's will (demonstrated by repeated failure at controlled use), then "disease" is the best name we have for what happens to alcoholics.

5

Self Deception and Self Diagnosis

"Diagnosis" comes from ancient Greek, and it means to know something "clean through." Diagnosing is a doctor's task, and given the complexity of the health care field, only a trained professional can make a diagnosis in many cases. Chemical dependency, however, is different. It is a disease for which the patient, not the doctor, makes the critical diagnosis. It is peculiar in another sense too. Treatment for alcoholism begins not after the diagnosis is made as with other diseases. Treatment begins the moment the patient asks himself this question, "Am I an alcoholic?"

Self Diagnosis: Recovery from chemical dependency is based on this axiom: *No one solves a problem he does not have.* The first step to solving a problem is to *have* one. As this applies to health care, the axiom means that patients comply with a recommended treatment only if they believe they have the disease for which the treatment is recommended. Applied to alcoholism, recovery begins when a drinker makes his first honest attempt to determine if drinking causes his problems.

Self-diagnosis is a long and bumpy road. First, an alcoholic must stop blaming others and acknowledge that it is his own behavior that is his problem. Only after that, is he ready to consider whether drinking plays a part in the problem, at the very least, that drinking is tangent to that problem. Next, he must conclude that drinking causes problems. And finally he must realize that drinking causes problems not by chance but because he is not in control of his drinking. He is "powerless." A doctor may tell a patient that he *appears* powerless, but only the patient knows it *"clean through."*

Self-diagnosis is so important that the Alcoholics Anonymous twelve step program begins with it:

> **"We admitted we were powerless**
> **over alcohol; that our lives had**
> **become unmanageable."**

Recovery begins when an alcoholic acknowledges that his life is "unmanageable," and that will power by itself fails to solve his problem.

"At Gut Level":   Addiction goes "clean through." Its denial goes deep. Self-diagnosis is not a casual musing. It is a gut level conviction. The following statements seem like honest self assessment at first glance. A closer look reveals they have little to do with diagnosis, nothing to do with disease, and even less to do with addiction.

> I drink too much.
> I have a drinking problem.
> I have a mild case of alcoholism.
> My family thinks I have a problem.
> I get drunk too often.
> When I drink, I have problems.
> I should stop drinking or drug taking.
> I am ashamed of my drinking.
> I feel guilty about it.

None of these statements says, "I am powerless. " And when a life of abstinence is the next step, only gut level conviction of powerlessness provides the basis for that step. The individual who succeeds at it sounds very different:

I have tried will power. Will power doesn't work. My
   drinking is beyond that.

I don't *have* alcoholism; I *am* an alcoholic.

This is not a habit; it's a compulsion.

My addiction is not in a bottle. It is in me.

No one is to blame. No one made me this way. I didn't try
   to become alcoholic, but that is what I am.

My problem doesn't come and go; it keeps getting worse.

The conviction that I am powerless is based on my track
   record with alcohol and drugs.

I am powerless. After a first drink (dose, hit, or snort), my
   drinking is unpredictable. And by itself, will power
   cannot keep me from that first one.

In A. A., the slogan, "The soberer you get, the drunker you were"
suggests that recovery is a process, denial erodes, and acceptance is
a dawning. In fact, acceptance sometimes takes years and continues
well into abstinent recovery. Professionals who work with addicts
in the early stages of treatment frustrate themselves when they try to
force the process. At the beginning, a professional helps a patient by
helping him see the need to take a hard look at his drinking. He can
point out the wisdom of remaining abstinent while doing so. He can
help the patient sort through layers of denial. But self-diagnosis is so
scary a process that it cannot be rushed.

There has been interest in the treatment community in the topic
of relapse. Books are written about it. Treatment centers offer programs designed specifically for relapsed patients. Workshops teach
counselors how to identify it and intervene in it. Theories about it
are plentiful. Not enough is said, however, about the one feature
which plays a major role in relapse during early recovery – and that
is failure at gut level self-diagnosis. There might be plenty of reasons
an alcoholic *wants* to drink, but the chief reason he *does* drink is that
he believes he can get away with it. In his mind there is little risk
involved in fooling with alcohol. He supposes he will manage in-

toxication and stop when he must. Any alcoholic who claims he will
have a little slip and get back to recovery believes he is in control of
the slip. He does not consider himself powerless. And that's denial,
plain and simple.

Any therapist who works in a psychiatric hospital is familiar with
the addicted patient hospitalized for treatment of a mental or emotional disorder a year or more after he has gotten sober. A number
of these dually afflicted patients know well that no matter how painful their psychiatric problems, they cannot afford to drink to relieve
them. Though they need relief, hospitalization is a more acceptable
alternative than drinking as a way to get relief because they know at
gut level they cannot control drinking. Their recovery is based on the
conviction that they are powerless. They also convince the rest of us
that "powerless over alcohol" is not synonymous with "helpless."

Keeping It Simple: The question of whether one is an addict
                              is difficult enough without cluttering the
mind with other questions which confuse the issue and subvert the
candor of the process. Self-assessment is more likely to be an honest
process if its focus is as simple as this.

Am I an alcoholic?

Two other questions, if considered simultaneously, cloud the issue. "What is alcoholism; is it a disease?" and, "Will I do anything
about it; will I stop drinking and seek help?" If one asks himself
these questions at the same time as he is trying to figure out if he is
alcoholic, his answers to questions about symptoms will be complicated at the very least, and quite probably distorted. The reason is
simple. If someone suspects his problem is a moral problem, he is
likely to be too ashamed to admit it. If he decides ahead of time that
either he cannot or will not stop drinking, he will virtually be forced
into deceiving himself about whether he is symptomatic for a disease
which requires abstinence. Few people want to regard themselves
as intentionally self-destructive, which indeed they would be if they

refused to treat a fatal disease. It is easier on the psyche to believe that one does not have a disease than to believe he does but refuses to do anything about it. Finally, those who believe alcoholism is a psychiatric disorder may be convinced that they drink to relieve its pain. For self-assessment to be an honest process it has to be a simple one. The central question is "Do I have the disease?"

Requirements for Self-Assessment: Chemical dependency requires three conditions in the person trying to self diagnose: honesty, willingness, and abstinence. Since denial plays so key a role in addiction, self-diagnosis requires one to double his efforts at self honesty. Blackouts, repression and euphoric recall make an alcoholic's memory not his most useful tool in reconstructing his past. Thus, he may need help from others to reconstruct it accurately.

Willingness! The question of whether one is an alcoholic cannot be answered as a favor to someone else. It cannot be answered because a family member or a judge thinks it wise. An alcoholic must answer the question for himself and for no reason other than that knowing the truth is critical.

Dry! Clean and sober is the only condition for a brain to be in while its owner tries to decide if he is addicted. The diagnostic decision is literally a *vital* one, and life and death issues are best considered undrugged. This does not apply to psychiatric medication, such as anti-depressants, anti-psychotics and mood stabilizers. And if someone is uncertain about whether to stop a medication which has been prescribed for him, he should consult with a psychiatrist familiar with addiction. Alcoholism counselors generally recommend a drug free period of ninety days while the individual is self-assessing. And if someone tries to remain abstinent for ninety days but fails, he has a problem. His problem is that he has not done what he has wanted to do, and at the very least will have to wonder why. Addiction may be the answer.

Another reason it is important to abstain while self-diagnosing is not so obvious. There is an inherent contradiction in the person who believes that he decides to drink while he is trying to figure out if his drinking is, in fact, compulsive. The person who "decides" to drink has already determined that his drinking is volitional, an act of will. He already believes that drinking is a choice he makes. In that frame of mind he cannot conclude that drinking is compulsive. It simply cannot be both a *decision* and a *compulsion* at the same time.

The Difficulties of Self Diagnosis: Addiction is tough to recover from because self-diagnosis is not only a requisite process; it is a devilishly difficult one. Six features make it so:

- To determine whether he has a drug problem, one must use the very brain which the drug has affected.

- To become an addict, one must cultivate a denial system. The very mind that has learned to deny the problem is the mind that has to be used to assess the problem.

- Addiction is insidious; it is hard to diagnose even by experts.

- Community drinking customs make distinguishing normal from abnormal drinking difficult.

- A defensive mind becomes proficient at maneuvering. This keeps addicts in denial.

- Fear and pride make self-diagnosis traumatic.

A Drugged and Drug-Affected Brain

Chemical Dependency is perverse. An addict in search of his symptoms is a person reviewing drugged experience with a drug-affected brain. The very memory which the disease distorts is the memory that must be used to reconstruct its history and diagnose it. Memories filter through the haze of a drug. Blackouts interfere with the process, making it impossible to interpret the meaning of an experience if one has no memory of having had the experience in the first place. Many experiences which an alcoholic does remember happened while he was drunk. Thus, his version of them is different from the version of others who were sober at the time. The same incident recalled by two heads, one clear and the other fogged, is recalled quite differently. Similarly, alcoholics are often surprised to learn that others viewed their drunkenness as extreme when they thought they had hidden it quite well. Recovering alcoholics find photographs taken of them when they were drunk and are amazed at how "out of it" they looked while at the time they thought they were quite debonair.

A Denying Mind

What makes self-diagnosis doubly perverse is that addiction cannot develop unless one learns to deny it. Self-deception becomes an established mechanism in the very mind which must get past self-deception. An alcoholic believes it when he says:

I am not an alcoholic.

I do not have a very big problem.

I may have a problem, but it will pass. It's a phase.

If it does not pass, it has nothing to do with drinking. I need counseling, but not for drinking.

If it does concern drinking, I'm not addicted to alcohol. I just drink too much.

Even if it is alcoholism, I can handle it. I don't need help.

The major difference between smart alcoholics and dumb ones is that smart ones stay sicker longer. Those who are good at semantic maneuvering and subtle distinctions have abundant means for prolonging denial. Intelligence is no advantage in getting through denial. It has proven to be a fatal disadvantage.

A Subtle and Insidious Disease

Diagnosing alcoholism is difficult too because by its nature it is insidious - difficult to see. Alcoholism progresses in one of two ways:

either so gradually that it is imperceptible (like aging), or so quickly (symptoms for some have been present from the outset of drinking) that it seems normal, common, not extraordinary at all. Instant alcoholics, so-called because they have been symptomatic from the start, fail to consider themselves as having a drinking problem because their drinking has always been the same. It takes a while for a person to realize his behavior is abnormal if he has never known what normal is.

Community, Social and Cultural Customs

Community customs too can make self-assessment difficult. Extreme versions of alcoholism have always been better box office draw at the movies than the stories of garden-variety alcoholics. A functioning alcoholic will fail to diagnose himself if he fails to fit what society presents on screen as a template for alcoholism. When television depicts heavy drinking as an accepted part of American socializing, it muddles the distinction between social drinking, heavy drinking and pathological drinking. At least every several years, television situation comedies present pathological drinking as commonplace and funny. Finally, alcoholics drift toward each other. In a room of abnormal drinkers, abnormal drinking does not seem abnormal. In short, a community helps addicts deny the problem by a patchwork of community denial, including the very way society perceives and presents normal alcohol use.

The Habit of Defensiveness

A disease which involves an increasingly intensive system of denial creates reasoning which is convoluted, and an approach to semantics and causation which splits hairs. Addicts get quite concrete and literal when it comes to questions about their drinking. They become so fixed on the nuance of a single word that they miss the intent of an entire question.

Alcoholics Anonymous distributes twenty questions to those trying to self -diagnose. According to the accompanying instructions, if one question is answered "yes," it is a warning that you are alcoholic. Two "yes" answers, and chances are that you are alcoholic. Three or more affirmative answers and you are "definitely" alcoholic. In the thick of denial an addict answering those twenty questions sounds like a defense attorney. For instance, when asked whether he loses time from work *due to drinking,* he answers that he loses time *due to sickness* but not *due to drinking,* somehow convincing himself that to answer "yes" would mean that he missed work because he had gotten drunk that morning.

Question 7 asks, "Do you turn to lower companions and an inferior environment when drinking?" The evasive answer is that he doesn't "*turn*" to such companions; he just "*ends up*" there. He might even counterattack by claiming that anyone who calls his companions lower is a bigot.

Question 10 asks if he craves a drink at a definite time daily, and is answered "no" by an alcoholic whose image of craving is so extreme (eyes bugged out, tongue drooping, crawling on hands and knees, and drooling) that no one would fit such a description. Craving is pictured in whatever way that does not fit the answerer.

Question 16 asks, "Do you drink alone"? The question is answered "no" if anyone at all is home, even though they are asleep. It is possible to drink alone at the Rose Bowl in the midst of 80,000 people. Lone drinking happens frequently in bars in fact.

The twenty questions are reprinted here. Spend a few moments reading over the questions and take the test.

1. Do you lose time from work due to drinking?

2. Is drinking making your home life unhappy?

3. Do you drink because you are shy with other people?

4. Is drinking affecting your reputation?

5. Have you ever felt remorse after drinking?

6. Have you gotten into financial difficulties as a result of drinking?

7. Do you turn to lower companions and an inferior environment when drinking?

8. Does your drinking make you careless of your family's welfare?

9. Has your ambition decreased since drinking?

10. Do you crave a drink at a definite time daily?

11. Do you want a drink the next morning?

12. Does drinking cause you to have difficulties in sleeping?

13. Has your efficiency decreased since drinking?

14. Is drinking jeopardizing your job or business?

15. Do you drink to escape from worries or troubles?

16. Do you drink alone?

17. Have you ever had a complete loss of memory as a result of drinking?

18. Has your physician ever treated you for drinking?

19. Do you drink to build up your self confidence?

20. Have you ever been to a hospital or institution on account of drinking?

Clarification of a few questions might be helpful. Question 2 may be answered differently by a drinker than by his spouse and children. Consider how family members would answer that and some of the other questions. When Question 5 asks if you have ever felt remorse after drinking, one should answer "yes" if he felt guilty not only about *how much he drinks* but also about his behavior when under the influence.

To answer Question 6, one must consider not only how much money he spends for alcohol but also how much he spends on the lifestyle which goes with it, the cost of repairing the damage drinking has caused, and the cost of necessary health care because of it. Addicts are shocked when they add up the hidden costs of a single year of addiction.

For Questions 9 and 13, it is necessary to take a long look back at an entire history to see what has happened to ambition and efficiency over that time.

Concerning Question 10, if one has difficulty seeing he craves a drink at a definite time, he should consider how he acts and feels if deprived of it at that time.

Question 11 doesn't ask if you have a drink; it asks if you want one. Many an alcoholic considers himself a problem drinker but not an alcoholic if he has gotten by without an eye-opener though he both needed and wanted it.

Question 12 is easy to gloss over. The question tries to get at whether drinking interferes with normal sleep in any way. Additional questions along the same lines include: Do you have trouble falling asleep unless you take a drink or a drug? Do you awaken in the middle of the night feeling nervous and needing something to calm down to get back to sleep? Do you fall asleep and awaken, or do you pass out and come to?

"Yes" is the answer to Question 14 for anyone who has lost his job because of drinking. "Yes" is also the appropriate answer for anyone whose job performance or business judgment has been affected by drinking. "Yes" is the accurate answer for anyone who is more preoccupied with drinking, than with his job.

Anyone who has been admitted to a hospital for the treatment of alcoholism should answer Question 20 in the affirmative, just as it should by anyone who has been treated in an emergency room because of a drunken accident at home, at work, or in a car.

There is nothing fool proof about a pencil and paper test. Tests do not make decisions; test takers do. One's score on this test is simply the sum of the number of times he or she has said "yes" to significant symptoms of alcoholism. The important conclusion is the one the test taker reaches after he knows his score.

There are, of course, people who are so suggestible that no matter what test they take, they end up considering themselves as having the pathology the test is supposed to reveal. Suggestible people should get help from an addiction's specialist rather than trust their own judgment in the assessment process. But because denial is so strong in chemical dependency, there is greater chance that a self-report questionnaire will fail to diagnose thousands who have the disease than over-diagnose thousands who don't.

Fear and Pride

Finally, self-diagnosis is fraught with fear and pride, powerful feelings which make the process stressful. Given alcoholism's reputation, few people are eager to admit having it. Centuries ago, Sophocles called pride the great destroyer of men. Today it destroys its share of alcoholics. Fear plays a role too. The future for a recovering alcoholic is a life of abstinence. Some alcoholics avoid starting the diagnostic process because they are afraid they are incapable of doing what the result of the process may require.

Proof Positive? Alcoholics are visible. Alcoholism is not. The naked eye can see addictive behavior, but what the eye sees is not addiction itself. One can be certain he has a scarred liver, but cirrhosis is the result of alcoholism, not alcoholism itself. There is yet no way to observe this disease directly. There is no organ which when examined under a microscope either proves or disproves the presence of the disease. Some souls torture through the debate about whether they are alcoholic, yearning for direct, positive, unequivocal, physical evidence to decide the issue for them once and for all. No such evidence exists. It may never. The only certainty one can have is moral certainty.

Some of alcoholism's symptoms are telling and almost always point to that diagnosis. Delirium Tremens (DTs), a profound complication of withdrawal, does not happen on a regular basis to non-alcoholics. DTs virtually clinches the diagnosis, but DTs occur in a small percentage of cases. And even among that number, incredible as it seems, there are those who have suffered DTs who still resist believing they are alcoholic. They reason that other medical problems might cause them to be delirious, shaky, dehydrated, hallucinatory and disoriented. Such reasoning would astonish emergency room doctors if it were rare.

Alcoholism is like the sun, too bright to look at. Nevertheless, one can be certain the sun is in the sky even though he has not looked directly at it. He knows it through shadows it casts on the ground, through the heat it generates, and through its reflection in windows.

The only certainty we can have of alcoholism's presence is the same - through signs.

Two Common Mistakes: An alcoholic looks for loopholes. Anyone who plows through the symptoms presented in the next chapter should be warned about two common mistakes alcoholics make. The first is to confuse symptoms with causes. The erroneous thinking goes something like this:

> Alcoholics wreck cars.
> I have never wrecked a car.
> Therefore, I am not an alcoholic.

The fallacy of the logic is that it assumes that all alcoholic wreck cars, and that it is the wrecking of a car which makes one an alcoholic. Alcoholics do not become alcoholics because they smash cars; they wreck cars because they are alcoholic. Drinking in the morning does not cause alcoholism. It works the other way around.

The second mistake is an all or nothing approach. That is, if one doesn't have *all* of the symptoms of a disease, then he doesn't have the disease. A drinker who fits every criterion in the Diagnostic Manual for substance dependence except one is very likely to focus on that one and conclude he is diagnosis free. In a list of sixty-five symptoms a denying alcoholic is drawn to those several symptoms which he has not experienced and creates those symptoms as the *absolute*, the *sine-qua-non* of alcoholism. Alcoholics who do not drink in the morning consider morning drinking to be "real" alcoholism.

No single symptom clinches the diagnosis. The absence of a single symptom does not rule alcoholism out. Nor does the presence of a single symptom automatically rule it in. Only a pattern of symptoms which persist over time provides the basis for the diagnosis.

Only on the basis of a broad pattern of symptoms and good history taking is a trained diagnostician able to avoid mistaking alcoholism for depression or vice-versa. Poor appetite, sleep difficulty, suicidal ideation, loss of pleasure, slowed response, impotence and depressed mood might indicate that an individual suffers either from an affective disorder, such as depression, or from a substance abuse disorder, such as alcoholism. By themselves, these symptoms are not conclusive of alcoholism. Only when they are accompanied by other symptoms, such as tolerance, blackouts, liver disease, legal difficulties and marital problems caused by drinking, is it reasonable to conclude that alcoholism plays the causative role. And for an alcoholic who becomes depressed after a period of treated abstinence, it is essential to treat his depression as existing along with his alcoholism, rather than instead of it.

Alcoholism is capable of imitating every one of depression's usual symptoms. And what appears to be depression is sometimes so indistinguishably intertwined with and clouded by alcohol and drug use, that only a period of total abstinence under the supervision of a psychiatrist familiar with the ordinary depression that occurs in early recovery can determine whether a patient suffers from depression, alcoholism, or both.

Alcoholism's diagnosis can be tricky.

6

SIGNS AND SYMPTOMS

Blackouts and seizures are symptoms of alcoholism. So are guilt and pancreatitis. Addiction causes trouble at home and at work. It keeps police departments busy. It affects health.

Categories of Symptoms: Alcoholism produces such a range of symptoms that their sheer number and variety can easily overwhelm anyone trying to wade through them in order to figure out whether he or she is alcoholic and/or drug addicted. Some symptoms occur because drugs affect the human brain and others because addiction creates behaviors which are typical of it. There are symptoms that suggest that drinking interferes with one's ability to perform his expected social roles and responsibilities. Drugs create health problems. The following categories are intended to simplify symptoms according to five types:

Nervous system symptoms are those which arise because mood-altering drugs affect the brains of susceptible individuals in unusual and pathological ways. Tolerance and withdrawal are symptoms of this type.

Behavioral is a name given to symptoms which indicate that someone thinks, feels, and acts like someone who has alcoholism.

Conflict signs - When a person is conflicted about his drinking, that conflict signifies a problem.

Social Consequences - As addiction progresses it interferes with one's ability to perform his role as citizen, family member, employee and student.

Health Consequences - Abusive drug use damages the body.

Some symptoms fit easily into the above categories, while others do not. A few symptoms can be placed in more than one category. Depression and paranoia, for example, result either from the effect drugs have on the brain or from the impact addiction has on the mind over a period of years. Psychiatrists rightly conclude that drugs cause paranoia and depression if those problems disappear when drugs are stopped. And if those problems persist after abstinence, the affected individual either has additional problems along psychological lines, or his depression and paranoia are the lasting scars of years of drug addiction.

Suicidal behavior might be listed as a "nervous system" sign since some addicts report feeling suicidal only when under the influence of a drug. However, when someone has lost his job, his family, and his self respect because of drinking, he may be suicidally depressed many weeks after he has gotten sober. "Relief drinking" and "outbursts of anger" fit several categories as well.

Nervous System Symptoms: Drugs affect the nervous system in ways which indicate that one's use of them is abnormal. When someone flies into a rage from drinking a sedative drug, such as alcohol, that ought to clue the drinker that his response to a depressant is not normal. The development of drug tolerance means an individual is adapting to a drug in a way which is bound to cause problems in the future if it hasn't done so already. Symptoms of withdrawal are proof positive that an individual has become so dependent that he must maintain a drug level, or suffer discomfort. Overdose is an extraordinary experience, which must be considered symptomatic of a larger problem. This is especially so when it happens repeatedly.

Different classes of drugs produce similar symptoms but in different ways. Alcohol, for instance, causes hallucinations when someone who is dependent on it stops drinking abruptly. Stimulant drug users hallucinate because they ingest too much drug, not because they stopped it. Physically dependent alcoholics get shaky when their level of alcohol drops, but cocaine snorters gets shaky because they snort too much of that stimulant.

Nervous system signs include:

Increased Need. Over time, an addict finds he needs more of a drug than he did previously, and so he or she drinks before a party, gulping or sneaking a drink. He hides his drinking, embarrassed by how much he drinks. He avoids non-drinking situations and seeks drinking ones. He craves, needs, or uses alcohol daily.

Loss of Control. Describes that phenomenon in which an initial drink, snort or dose starts a process which ends in acute and unintended intoxication and unpredictable behavior. *Loss of control* is more apparent with some drugs than with others. It is more apparent, for instance, with cocaine than with marijuana. In a single night, a cocaine addict may snort what was meant to last a weekend. *Loss of control* is progressive; it worsens over time. It is the reason alcoholics wind up drunk at the wrong time in the wrong place. It explains why they drink more than they promise, and why they are unable to predict on any occasion how much they will drink, for how long, and what will happen as a result. Inability to refrain is another meaning that has been assigned to loss of control. As addiction progresses, an addict finds it more and more difficult to stay away from his stuff.

Tolerance. One is tolerant if he needs more alcohol to produce a desired effect, or when the same dose produces less effect than it did previously. Even alcoholics who report high tolerance at the outset of drinking nevertheless report increased tolerance over the years. It is impossible to determine if someone is drug tolerant on the basis of the effect a drug has from one night to the next since several factors influence how drunk one *feels* on any given occasion. Tolerance is presumed only under similar conditions and over a period of a year. With the same drug potency, same rate of consumption, same physical health, same mind set, and same setting, a tolerant drinker finds that he is less intoxicated, less impaired, less drugged than he was previously. Thus, he must drink more to get the old effect. Eventually tolerance reverses, and low doses produce dramatic results. Someone who claims booze has stopped working is in reality acknowledging that he has become tolerant.

Blackouts. Blacking out is not passing out. A blackout is a period of amnesia while under the influence. In a blackout, a drinker does not remember several hours of an evening, or driving home, or both. Blackouts may be dramatic or uneventful, such as two hours of an evening, or a trip of several days and hundreds of miles missing from memory. A blackout drinker may be able to reconstruct an experience based on what others tell him about it, but he will never recall the experience.

Relief Drinking. Using alcohol or another "recreational" drug for its tranquilizing effect is called relief drinking. It is using a "social" drug as if it were a "prescription" drug. Whatever else relief drinking might be called, it is not social. To drink in order to calm down, to induce sleep, or to relieve depression is to use alcohol as a sleeping pill, a tranquilizer, or an antidepressant. Someone who regularly drinks before a public performance or lovemaking ought to wonder if such drinking points to a problem. The irony of relief drinking is that much of it aims at relieving problems which drinking itself has created over time.

Jekyll-Hyde Reaction. Jekyll-Hyde describes a sudden change in personality while consuming alcohol. It is not to be confused with "personality change," which is discussed later. Jekyll-Hyde describes the sudden onset of rage, especially alarming from someone for whom it is atypical when sober. Outbursts of anger and brush fire fury are peculiar responses to a sedative drug.

Impotence and Decreased Interest in Sex. The notion that alcoholic women are nymphomaniacs is a male fantasy. Both men and women may be less inhibited love makers because booze loosens, but from a biomechanical point of view they are not better performers because of it. They may think they are better sex partners when "looped" for the same reason that they may think they are better drivers. The truth is that they are simply less uptight. They are not better performers. In advanced stages alcoholics, have another love.

Suicidal Behavior. In early addiction, suicidal behavior occurs usually only when an individual is drunk. Later on, suicidal thoughts, gestures and attempts happen even when one is abstinent because of the mounting effects of drug, depression, shame, and loss.

Cognitive Problems. Short-term memory deficits, all or nothing thinking, indecision, and shortened attention span signify chemical dependency's damaging effect on the brain.

Emotional Augmentation. Emotional augmentation describes overreaction to stress or sadness, such as overly intense feelings in situations not connected in a personal way to the individual. Feelings are intensified by a drug-agitated nervous system.

The Shakes. Individuals who are withdrawing from a sedative drug get the shakes, which are experienced at first as inner tremulousness. But eventually, the shakes become visible as hand tremors. When caused by alcohol, shakes begin twenty-four hours after the last drink. With other depressants, withdrawal's onset may be delayed for as long as seven to nine days. Stimulant drug users feel shaky from too much stimulant.

Convulsions. Seizures may occur during sedative drug withdrawal. They look and sound like epileptic "fits." Seizures also occur from excessive doses of stimulants.

Hallucinations. During sedative withdrawal, an individual may "see" and "hear" things which are not there. Hallucinations result from excessive doses of stimulants and of course hallucinogens as well.

Delirium Tremens ("DTs"). The DTs are more than a hallucinatory experience combined with shakes. Delirium Tremens describes a profound medical condition, such as confusion, disorientation, a medical crisis, which is a life threatening complication of withdrawal from alcohol.

Fear. A sense of "impending doom," the feeling one is losing his mind, an overwhelming sense of panic, and gripping fear that a catastrophe is imminent. All indicate a drinker or drugger is suffering from the long-term effects of drugs.

The Behavioral Signs: Symptoms are called behavioral because they represent how alcoholics and addicts behave during addiction. They are the psychological results of chemical dependency.

It is a mistake to think that because chemical dependency produces behavioral and psychological symptoms that underlying psychological problems cause it. A diabetic in crisis looks psychologically disturbed, but he is not. Addicts behave strangely under the influence of drugs. Depression and paranoia do result from the toxic effect drugs have on a human brain as much as from the inner turmoil that addiction produces. More often than not the causes of an addict's behavior are twofold: biochemical and emotional. When someone's emotional well being depends on his using drugs, he will act in unusual ways just to get drugs. If, in addition, he needs drugs to stave off withdrawal, his behavior may be downright bizarre.

Psychological or behavioral signs include:

Denial. Denial is not the product of stupidity. Denial is the mechanism the mind uses to keep a painful reality at bay. Alcoholics minimize their drinking and trivialize the problems and feelings resulting from it. Their memories of unpleasant experiences and past confrontations are suppressed. Sometimes they are even repressed. Denial means that an addict fails to perceive that he has a problem. It does not mean that he knows the truth and deliberately tells lies.

Rationalization. When compulsion is its cause, a drinker must create all sorts of excuses for why he drinks and drugs as much, and as often, as he does. Alcoholics blame drinking and drunkenness on all sorts of people, places and things. Quite understandably, addicts believe their problems cause their drinking and drug use, rather than the other way around.

Projection. When a person finds a trait in himself he dislikes or despises, he is liable to reject that trait psychologically. The mind, however, will not always allow him to get away with it. And so, he ends up seeing that trait in others. This is projection. An angry alcoholic sees other drunks as angry. He sees drinking itself as an expression of anger. Some alcoholics are adept at diagnosing alcoholism in others.

Sensitivity about One's Use. Drinking eventually becomes a touchy subject. Alcoholics stop bragging about their drinking and start lying about it.

Anxiety. Attacks of worry, fear that they will be "found out," and free-floating anxiety characterize alcoholics and addicts.

Ego-Centeredness. After years of swinging between the grandiosity and the humiliation which out of control drinking creates, addicts become ego centered. A "great big I" and a "poor little me" are ego extremes. Sober periods are excruciatingly self-conscious for some.

Depression. Depression is one of the masks alcoholism wears. Even for a garden variety alcoholic, depression may come about because of drug use, the cumulative losses he has suffered and/ or the impact addiction has on confidence and self-esteem. Alcoholism imitates all of depression's clinical symptoms: loss of appetite due to stomach irritation, disturbed sleep due to withdrawal, impotence, suicidal thinking, and loss of interest and energy.

Low Self Esteem. Alcoholics eventually feel worthless, inadequate, and even self-hating. Low self-esteem sometimes hides behind bravado and superficial confidence. For some addicts, work achievement and career success compensate for feelings of worthlessness. For others, the impact addiction has on self-esteem is obvious. One of the myths associated with causes of addiction is that low self esteem causes it. You will win your bet more often, however, if you bet that alcoholism causes low self esteem.

Loss of Confidence. This problem becomes obvious when the drinker believes that he can no longer do what he used to do with ease.

Personality Changes. This is not the Jekyll-Hyde reaction mentioned earlier, but a more gradual change in personality which occurs over years. Addicts become moody, apathetic, sarcastic, self-pitying, resentful, depressed, grandiose, antisocial, bitter and cynical.

"Telephonitis." Intoxicated, often late at night, addicts call up their friends and relatives. The reasons appear to be three-fold: an attempt to break free from the isolation one feels ("I had to talk to someone"); a cry for help; and a means of dissipating feelings of guilt. Sometimes the call is made during a blackout.

Control Ploys. As control erodes, alcoholics try a range of ploys to limit drinking and avoid acute intoxication. A common ploy is postponing drinking until after 6:00 p.m. or limiting it to weekends. A list of such ploys is included and explored more fully in Chapter 7.

Maturation Problems. Addiction arrests emotional growth. Incredible as it seems, there are addicts who have never interacted at a social gathering without a drink or drug for all of their entire adult lives. Some find it difficult to remember when they experienced an emotion from beginning to end without being under the influence somewhere along the line. When feelings are learned under the influence, even alcoholics who are competent in the world of business wind up emotionally immature, emotionally younger than their business acumen and their chronological years would indicate. As addiction progresses, maturity regresses. Addicts become demanding, stubborn and immature - the terrible twos in the terrible forties.

Resentment. Resentment is anger's first cousin. It is re-feeling old anger from a past injustice or injury. Resentment may be genuine and justified, or manufactured and exaggerated. Whichever they are, resentments play an interesting dual role in chemical dependency which is further discussed in Chapter 7.

Self Pity. Self-pity is the "poor me" feeling. It looks at what is missing from our lives. Self-pity is often a mask which resentment wears. Beneath self-pity, lies resentful feelings toward the people and institutions believed responsible for injustice and injury.

Suspiciousness. Suspiciousness in alcoholics can reach paranoid levels causing some to even carry guns because of it.

Mistrust. Those who hide their feelings are liable to believe that others do the same, thus doubting the sincerity of others. Hypocrisy which is despised in oneself is projected onto others, further complicating trust. Their own increasing cynicism leads alcoholics to question the motives of others.

Obsession with Alcohol and/or Drugs. This is another symptom which gets progressively worse over time. Addicts start out looking forward to their drinking and drug use. It then becomes a preoccupation, which finally ends up as an obsession. Drinking, once merely one of life's many recreations, becomes its main activity.

Inner Conflict: The clash between drunken behavior and personal values gives rise to another set of signs. Social drinkers are not ashamed of how much or how often they drink. Addicts are, and it is this shame which indicates that their drinking is abnormal. Some of addiction's signs indicate that drinking leads to feelings of guilt and shame and attempts to deal with guilt and shame.

Guilt. Guilt about drinking, its amount and frequency, as well as outrageous, immoral, and/or illegal behavior point to an alcohol and/or drug problem.

Shame. Shame is the emotion a person experiences when he believes he has transgressed his own principles and is afraid others will find out. Shame results not only from what alcoholics do when they are drunk, but also from what they fail to do because of their preoccupation with drinking.

Remorse. From Latin, "remorse" means "to die again." It is the persistence of deep guilt and shame.

Alienation and Isolation. Addicts avoid social contact in order to avoid the shame and embarrassment of having their behavior compared to that of others. There are some who choose to drink alone to avoid such feelings. Sooner or later addicts are so unpleasant to be around their friends avoid them. "Masking" such feelings increases an addict's emotional isolation.

Attempts "To Straighten Out." Guilt about his drinking along with the vague feeling he might have a problem are behind an alcoholic's initiating a program of exercise, health food, return to church, physical fitness and good books. Undoing of this sort serves an addict's denial in three ways: it helps him think he has his act together (short of not drinking); it reduces guilt, and it demonstrates to others and to himself that he doesn't have a problem. Attempts to straighten out include self-denying and even self-punitive measures. Alcoholics have even given up drinking for periods of time to prove they are okay.

Search for a Cure. Eventually an alcoholic's problem becomes apparent even to himself, and he does try to solve the problem. He does so, however, without considering drinking as the cause and without considering stopping it. Over his history, an alcoholic may go to a psychiatrist, psychologist or counselor for help with "personal" problems (but not for a drinking problem). He may see a marriage counselor, a family counselor, or a financial counselor. He may change jobs to get a fresh start, or move to a new city, called a "geographic cure." He may seek medical treatments, including tranquilizers for insomnia, anxiety or depression.

The Social Consequences: When a symptom is labeled a "social consequence" of addiction, what is meant is not that addiction affects one's party life, but that it affects the way he fails to carry out his role as spouse, parent, lover, citizen, worker, employee, student and/or neighbor.

Symptoms of this sort differ widely with individuals for obvious reasons. Unmarried people do not get divorced because of drinking. Non-drivers are not charged with driving while intoxicated (though they might well be charged with walking while intoxicated if it were an offense). Some alcoholics are fired from jobs, but self-employed alcoholics hardly even reprimand themselves for shoddy performance. Though the social consequences differ with individuals, loss of control makes it nearly impossible for an addict to escape every one of these consequences over time. The social consequences are as follows:

Family Problems. Separation and divorce. Physical and emotional abuse of spouses, children and parents. Children with emotional problems because of their parent's alcohol and drug problem. Parents with emotional problems because of their children's drug problems. Turmoil at home. Stress from living in an atmosphere tense with powerful and unpredictable emotions. Unexpected and undesirable family relocations.

Relationship Problems - Disturbed love relationships and friendships because of drunkenness and physical abuse. Inability to sustain relationships. Divorce. All come with addiction.

Legal Problems. Arrests for drunken driving, disturbing the peace, public intoxication, assault, and disorderly conduct. Law suits resulting from drugged and drug-affected behavior. Jail terms for crimes committed to secure illegal drugs or from using legal ones.

Financial Problems. The cost of alcohol and drugs. Mounting bills because of addiction. Insurance premium increases because of accidents. Extraordinary legal expenses. The costs of repairing or replacing a wrecked automobile, damaged household goods, and/or cigarette-burned clothing.

Household Problems. If the addicted person is the homemaker, the home is likely to be an unhealthy or unsafe environment because of carelessness and neglect. Other problems include burned and wasted food, the expense of buying easy to prepare, more costly foods, and the cost of dining out more than usual.

Job Problems. Absence and lateness. Demotions. Unwanted transfers. Loss of confidence. Conflict with co-workers. Complaints from customers and clients. Damaged reputation. Poor performance. Costly mistakes and errors in judgment. Lost jobs.

School Problems. Lateness, absence, poor grades, cheating, and/or copying homework because an alcoholic student is "too wasted" to do assignments at home are not uncommon for young alcoholics and other addicts. Some are suspended and expelled because of drinking and behavioral problems related to it. Reputation as a "head," "burnout," "boozer," "druggie," "drunk," "junkie" is another consequence for young addicts.

The Health Consequences:

Two different kinds of health problems result from drug abuse: *direct* damage to the body, such as diseases of the liver; and *indirect* consequences such as accidents, neglect and secondary illnesses. In an appendix to *Getting Them Sober, Volume 3*, no fewer than three hundred diseases and disorders are listed as secondary to alcoholism (Drews, 1983). The interested reader is referred to this as a list of potential health symptoms.

There is no way to predict which health problems any individual will suffer, since a number of variables play roles in causing such problems. These variables include: the particular drug an individual abuses and the risks associated with that drug; the frequency and amount of its use; the interaction between this drug and other drugs the individual uses; and finally, the state of the individual's health and his particular susceptibility to health problems.

Those curious about whether a medical problem is caused or exacerbated by drinking should consult a physician familiar with the diseases and disorders secondary to chemical dependency. One warning, however! If an addict goes to a physician who is not familiar with chemical dependency, or if he lies to his doctor about his drinking and drug use, he may leave the doctor's office with a prescription for a drug which is just as addictive as the one which caused him to go to the doctor in the first place. So many of the health consequences of alcohol or drugs beg for mood altering medication as the antidote, that it is quite easy for doctors to consider prescribing them. Anxiety, sleep disturbance, depression, impotence, irritability, mood swings, stomach distress, palpitations, paranoia, high blood pressure, panic attacks, and even persistent itching are a few of the health problems caused by alcoholism for which alcoholics have been given addictive substitutes as a remedy.

In addition to the direct harm drugs do to the body, there are indirect consequences like the twin menaces of accidents and neglect. Accidents are common. Addicts fall down stairs, walk into walls and run into cars – both as drivers and pedestrians. Alcoholics have caused explosions, boat crashes and industrial accidents. They have smashed through doors, tumbled out of windows, and fallen off of boats. They have stuck their hands into operating machinery and gotten their fingers clipped. They have stuck their noses into other people's business with similar results. Accidents caused by alcoholism would be funny if it were not for the numbers who are maimed and dead because of them, and if it were not for the losses to industry and to environments because of them.

Neglect of health is another of addiction's indirect consequences. Teeth rot. Gums swell. Corns harden. Vision blurs. Hearing deteriorates. Eyeglasses and hearing aids are lost and not replaced. Alcohol addicts procrastinate going to a doctor for so long that a minor problem grows to proportions which require a major medical intervention to correct it. AIDS has been added to the list of addiction's indirect but fatal consequences.

7

THE DYNAMICS OF DEPENDENCY

Addiction is a movie, not a photograph. It is a biography, not a portrait. Addiction plays out as a story with a beginning, middle, and an end. It is a narrative in which tolerance, cellular adaptation, growing dependence, cycles of symptoms, enablers, denial, and hopelessness play interactive roles. Drinking and problems get worse. Personalities deteriorate. To see just a slice of an alcoholic's life is quite misleading. To know an alcoholic is to know his whole history.

Not every story proceeds headlong into destruction. Some alcoholics get sick slowly and gradually. Other alcoholics can, and do, stop drinking for periods of time, though eventually they resume, and their drinking accelerates. There are others still whose drinking levels out and symptoms abate for periods of time. But addiction is progressive, and sooner or later, drinking increases and symptoms intensify.

The Forces of Dependency: Chemical dependency is a complex process with a range of brain and body changes which occur over time, reaching a finale in which persistent craving and severe withdrawal are the forces which drive it. Long before he gets the shakes, however, subtle forces drive an addiction. These forces are four-fold. Addictive drinking is cyclic; eventually drinking causes drinking. Next, denial grows thicker with the passing years. Enablers unwittingly help addiction continue. Hopelessness plays a role too.

Knowing the forces that drive addiction provides clues about how to intervene in the process. As long as an alcoholic drinks, he grows tolerant of alcohol and his brain adapts to that drug in problematic ways. Neither tolerance nor cellular adaptation will disappear spontaneously on its own. Only abstinence achieved either because an addict agrees to try it or because an authority enforces it moves an addict toward recovery. At least an abstinent alcoholic whose brain clears has a chance to see that he has a problem. Second, denial keeps alcoholics drinking, and so whatever erodes denial aids recovery. Enablers play a part in addiction's progression, and so getting enablers to stop enabling also aids recovery. And finally, hopelessness plays a role. Recovery that holds out the promise that life is at least bearable, actually possible, and even enjoyable, will motivate an alcoholic to pursue abstinence.

The Nuances of Its Progression: Because addiction happens to all sorts of people, it manifests with a range of individual nuances. No two stories are exactly alike (although their general outlines are remarkably similar). Alcoholics drink in different ways. Some like the "hard stuff"; others prefer beer. Still others prefer wine. Some alcohol addicts drink daily; others on weekends, and a few binge drink. Every addict has a favorite drug, a "drug of choice" and favorite companions, times, and places that go with it.

Individuals experience symptoms in different ways too. Addiction progresses from *symptomatic to problematic to compulsive* drug use for some. In other words, symptoms, such as tolerance and blackouts, are present from the beginning. But neither public problems result from drinking nor is drinking in any obvious way compulsive at the start. Only later does drinking cause problems, and only after that, does alcohol become an obsession and its use compulsive. For others the pattern is quite different. For them drinking is compulsive long before it causes problems. It simply grows more compulsive and, therefore, more problematic. And for a third group, problems occur right from the start. A drinker is charged with driving while intoxicated the very first year he drives a car. Despite the diversity of its individual progressions, alcoholism is predictable in its broadest outline.

Three Stages: Chemical Dependency is divided into the three stages of early alcoholism, middle stage and advanced symptoms, with specific pairs of symptoms marking the transition from one stage to the next. Early alcoholism ends and the middle stage begins when an alcoholic *loses control* and denies it. The middle stage ends and advanced symptoms begin once tolerance has developed and an attempt to stop drinking is followed by binge drinking.

Progressive Symptoms: Certain symptoms appear early on and reappear later each time worse than before. These are discussed first.

Tolerance

Alcoholics who start out with an early high tolerance for alcohol find nevertheless that their tolerance still increases. Thus, more of a drug is required to produce a desired effect. Eventually tolerance becomes quite unpredictable; the effect booze has from one night to the next is quite variable. Six drinks have no obvious effect one night, whereas a week later two drinks render the drinker dysfunctional. Finally, tolerance reverses, and small amounts produce disturbing results.

Tolerance is presumed either when the amount someone drinks has to increase if it is to achieve its desired effect, or when the effect diminishes despite consuming a constant amount. If last year it took four beers and now it takes eight to get a "buzz," that's tolerance. Or if the "buzz" grows fainter and fainter even though the amount remains constant, that's also tolerance.

Preoccupation

Preoccupation is another progressive symptom. Alcoholics deny, some to the very end, that they are preoccupied with drinking. However, *looking forward to drinking* becomes *preoccupation*, and *preoccupation finally becomes obsession* provided, of course, they live long enough.

Loss of control

Loss of control occurs with increasing frequency and unpredictability over time. At the start, alcoholics *lose control* once in a while. Later, control slips with greater frequency. At the end, control seems gone entirely, and drunkenness happens so regularly that alcoholics take precautions to insure their safety before setting out to drink. These precautions have been extreme. Some alcoholics have locked themselves in hotel rooms and mailed their car keys home to avoid endangering themselves while drunk.

Denial and Rationalization: Denial is not only a progressive symptom in alcoholism's history, it is essential to the very process which keeps that history moving. Denial aims not so much at deceiving others as deceiving oneself. Thus, intelligence is no protection against it. Smart addicts are simply better at denial than stupid ones.

Over time, the defenses an alcoholic employs take on a variety of forms. At the beginning, an alcoholic minimizes his drinking, problems and feelings ("**Minimizing**"). Later he blames others for his problems ("**Rationalization**"). Soon he speaks of his drinking in so general a way that any perceptible problem with it evaporates in a mist of words ("**Generalizing**"). He disjoints the incidents which make up his history, making each episode seem separate and unconnected ("**Narrow Focus**"). He intellectualizes the problems drinking causes ("**Intellectualization**") thereby keeping himself from feeling those problems **("Isolation of Affect")**. He misses the sweep of his symptoms by focusing only on recent ones. He rejects non-drinkers as prudish ("**Ridiculing**"). He gravitates to people who agree with and collude in his drinking ("**Allying**"). He distracts himself from his alcoholism by staying angry at all sorts of people for all sorts of reasons ("**Defocusing**"). He either finds or invents all sorts of excuses and explanations for his drinking and his problems ("**Rationalization**"). He becomes preoccupied with aches and pains; so that he has neither the time nor the energy to focus on the effect drinking has on him ("**Somatization**"). He claims that everyone drinks the way he does ("**Normalizing**"). He blocks the truth by ("**Fantasizing and Regressing**"). He focuses on peripheral issues in a fine rage; nonsmoking alcoholics lecture eloquently and myopically on the evils of nicotine ("**Displacement and Defocusing**"). In denial an alcoholic is more aware of those symptoms he has not experienced rather than those he has (the "**Nevers**"). Unpleasant memories of the consequences of his drinking are pushed down and pushed out of his conscious memory ("**Suppression and Repression**"). He jogs, eats nonfat yogurt, goes to church and reads good books - all to demonstrate he has no problem ("**Undoing**"). The result is his disease gets worse.

Early Stage Symptoms: Alcoholism is not set on course because prone individuals drink to escape reality. Ask a dozen alcoholics why they started drinking, and you are likely to get a dozen answers. Nearly all start for the same reasons non-alcoholics start - because it seemed adult, because it was offered, because they heard it made you feel good, because it seemed the time, because it was a way of bonding with peers, because they were shy, because friends drank, and sometimes simply because it was there. But, even though they have no unique reason for starting, alcoholics do end up drinking to escape reality. The irony is, of course, that they drink to escape the very reality which drinking created. Early symptoms include: blackouts; guilt and shame; tolerance; and drifting toward other addicts.

Blackouts

For some, blackouts occur early. Others do not blackout until the very end. Some experience blackouts throughout, while some never black out at all. When blackouts occur early they are often discounted, thought to be normal, as something which happens to everyone who drinks.

In our society, joking about blackouts is so common that partly for that reason alcoholics consider them insignificant. Only with alcohol is a rational person likely to dismiss sudden-onset amnesia as funny. If he were to suffer even brief memory lapses because of chocolate milk, he would be off to his doctor frantic for an explanation, and if told to stop drinking chocolate milk altogether, he would. But when he cannot remember an entire evening because of alcohol, he laughs it off. Some day statistics may tell us how common blackouts are among all drinkers. Whatever the truth, when blackouts happen at the start of chemical dependency, denying, minimizing and normalizing them sets a pattern for the future.

Guilt and Shame

When it comes to addiction, guilt has several origins and travels several paths. Alcoholics may feel guilty about drinking itself, sensing from the start that they drink too much or too often. When drunkenness causes foolish, silly or stupid behavior, even teenage alcoholics feel the pain. Despite pain, however, the drive to drink keeps him going to the liquor store regularly. At some point, he feels uneasy about even being seen there. By thirty, he is ashamed of neglecting those he loves. And by forty, his remorse is poignant when his drunkenness is out of control. The history of an alcoholic devotes several chapters to guilt alone.

Tolerance

It is a mistake to think that tolerance is a sign of advanced alcoholism. Most adults remember a classmate or two who could hold a lot of booze even as teenagers. It is not uncommon for youngsters who were tolerant from the start to mistake tolerance for alcohol as freedom from alcoholism, reasoning that if they can hold their booze they won't have a problem. But the alcoholic's problem is not, as the old saying goes, that he cannot hold his booze. His problem is that he can hold it - and much too much of it at that.

Drifting Toward Other Addicts

Drinkers gravitate to drinkers. Addicts find addicts. The process begins early, and the reasons are multiple. One individual's heavy drinking is easily masked in a room where everyone is a heavy drinker. Alcoholics who surround themselves with alcoholics find it easy to see their own drinking as normal. In a "world" of alcoholics, alcoholic drinking is the norm. There will always be a good supply in a room of heavy drinkers.

From Early to Middle Stage: When a drinker repeatedly explains away his drunkenness and his *loss of control,* and when he blames others for the problems which result from his drinking, addiction moves to another level, a more serious stage. Intervention by an outside agent becomes increasingly necessary to halt it. An alcoholic who believes he is not sick is powerless to stop being sick. Symptoms intensify.

Middle Stage: In the middle stage of the disease, an alcoholic's inability to control his drinking occurs with increased frequency. Family, job, marital and legal problems begin, increase or intensify. Addicts get sick emotionally. Their reasoning grows convoluted.

With denial in place, an alcoholic blames his drunkenness on almost anything but his own loss of control. If he cannot blame others he will be forced to see *loss of control* as the reason he ends up drinking, and that conclusion is unacceptable. Parental neglect and indifference, stressful jobs, disappointments in love, too strict an upbringing and early repressive religious education come in for a fair share of the blame as well.

Hiding Use

Eventually an alcoholic realizes he wants more booze than even he believes appropriate, causing him to become secretive about it. Sneaking into a bathroom to drink from a bottle hidden in a linen closet is one way of doing this. Pouring six ounces of booze into a glass and calling it a single drink is another. Drinking before arriving at a party is a third. Not all alcoholics hide bottles, although many hide how much and how often they drink.

Extravagance

As they get sicker, alcoholics are forced to prove to themselves and to others that they are neither sick nor bad. This "proof" may take the form of acts of generosity, which are sometimes quite extravagant. Alcoholics give of their time, money, and advice, unaware that part of their motivation is to prove they are not alcoholic. Christmas provides a perfect opportunity for an alcoholic to put on a display of opulence for his family. Giving lavish gifts and treating the family to an unexpected and expensive winter vacation helps him believe he is not in trouble with booze, while providing a reason to reward himself for being a good fellow - with a drink, of course. Alcoholism runs rampant at Christmas for reasons other than the general acceptability of drinking during that season. Addiction takes whatever opportunity life offers "to let her rip," and Christmas offers such opportunity. The structure of the work week keeps addiction in check, but on weekends and holidays drinking runs rampant. A summer vacation provides an opportunity for excess. A promotion is a good excuse to get plastered. A demotion serves equally as well. Alcoholics are magicians; they can turn anything into a drink.

The Role Resentment Plays

From the start, Alcoholics Anonymous recognized that resentment plays a major role in relapse. By harboring resentments, alcoholics shut themselves off from recovery and drink again (AA, 1976, pp. 64-66). Vernon Johnson, an early treatment practitioner, recognized that chemical dependency does more than trigger resentments. It creates the "more chronic condition of having become a resentful person." Johnson also recognized that without treatment, resentfulness would "drive the patient back into the bottle" (Johnson, 1973, pp. 78-79).

As addiction progresses, in part because the brain is poisoned, an alcoholic's resentments become persistent and obsessional. Angry feelings about past injustice, abuse or neglect, either real or trumped up, are resurrected and re-felt. To the casual observer, harping on old resentments seems to indicate that an alcoholic has personality problems. But the truth is that alcoholics harbor resentments because they are useful to them as alcoholics. Resentment is not coincidental to alcoholism; the role it plays is dynamic and twofold. First, resentments provide an alcoholic with an explanation for why his life is going so badly. Without implicating his drinking, he blames his current circumstances on past injustices and harms. Second, resentments provide an alcoholic with an excuse to drink. When he can find no other reason, resentment will provide an alcoholic with a ready-made excuse. "You'd drink too if you had a wife or a life like mine." Addiction is efficient; it wastes little energy; it uses whatever life puts at its disposal. With remarkable facility, addiction turns even justified, preexisting resentments into playing a chemical dependency role.

The dynamic relationship of resentment to active disease becomes apparent in recovery. Once he quits drinking, his head clears, and he accepts that drinking causes his problems, an alcoholic's resentments no longer serve a purpose. In many cases, those resentments dissipate. Resentments, harbored for years, have been known to disappear with no more treatment than abstinence. True, there are alcoholics for whom resentfulness has become so ingrained that extra help from a sponsor in A. A. or a counselor or therapist familiar with recovery is helpful to avoid the thin ice of early recovery. And there are, and probably always will be, addicts for whom resentfulness was present and disruptive in their lives before addiction became a problem, and additional therapy may be necessary for them once they are sober. Finally, there are recovering alcoholics who find that the conditions which foster resentment persist into recovery. An alcoholic whose family remains distant, controlling, bitter and mistrustful years after he has been sober may find that additional support and counseling is helpful in handling resentments which, if ignored, can create the conditions for relapse. Even in these cases, however, the intensity of resentment is not as powerful in a sober brain as it was in a drugged and drug-affected one.

Control Ploys

Eventually only the most intractable alcoholic will fail to realize he gets drunker than he intends and will make some effort to "limit" his drinking. What motivates such control ploys is that *loss of control* threatens to break through denial and into consciousness. Instead, he convinces himself that his excesses are of recent vintage and a matter of mere carelessness, and that all he has to do is get these recent excesses under control. And so, even as he establishes ploys to control his drinking, his denial keeps him from realizing why he must.

Control ploys are not intended to keep an alcoholic from drinking; they are meant to keep him from getting "too" drunk. What follows are familiar ploys with that purpose in mind. The list is worded with alcoholics, street and prescription addicts in mind. The ploys are occasionally funny; at times they are just plain astonishing.

- Switching from hard liquor to beer or wine.
- Switching to light beer.
- Switching brands of liquor or types of drug.
- Switching to a lower proof or a less potent drug.
- Postponing drinking until after dinner.
- Prolonging the interval between doses.
- Changing the times and places one drinks.
- Changing drinking companions.
- Carefully measuring drinks in a graded tumbler.
- Trying to skip a dose or a day.
- Going clean for the weekend.
- Keeping a careful written record of drinks or doses.
- Buying a fixed amount intending to limit use in that way.
- Refrigerating a fixed number of beers to limit use.
- Drinking and/or using only on weekends.
- Drinking and/or using only after noon.

- Alternating alcoholic with non-alcoholic drinks.
- Alternating more potent with less potent drugs.
- Keeping alcohol in inconvenient places so that it's hard to get.
- Trying to stick to weak drinks or mild drugs.
- Eating a full meal before drinking.
- Limiting the money one takes when going out.
- Supplementing alcohol with another drug.
- Stopping for a period of time to regain health.

One alcoholic kept booze in the trunk of his car so that drinking would be inconvenient, and thereby, limit the amount he drank. In the dead of winter he put on his overcoat, went out to the car, opened the trunk, got a bottle, brought it inside, poured a drink, returned the bottle to the trunk, and went back inside. Before the evening was over, either the bottle found its way inside permanently, or he drank curbside. Another alcoholic switched from home drinking to bar drinking, reasoning that bar drinks would be too expensive and that would limit how much he drank. Later he switched to home drinking blaming the bar's atmosphere for encouraging excess. He got as drunk in an easy chair as on a barstool. A third alcoholic changed drinking companions, blaming his buddies for getting him wasted only to find he got as wasted with new friends or even all alone. One alcoholic, in a familiar ploy, drank beer on weeknights, reserving hard liquor for the weekends so he would not be too hung over to go to work. Another (there are probably many) switched from Bourbon to Scotch because he had convinced himself that there was an ingredient in Bourbon which made him mean. He was right. He found the same ingredient in Scotch, Chablis, Vodka, and Malt Liquor. A high school student who was in treatment for alcoholism by the time she was eighteen, limited herself to three dollars whenever she went bar drinking, believing she would go home after her three dollars were spent. By day she was a good student, a better than average athlete, and well liked by her peers. By night she hustled male customers for drinks after her three-dollars had been spent. She ended the evening by vomiting. It was routine.

A prescription addict discovered he was too drugged to function in the middle of the day and so skipped his noon dose only to take double or triple doses at dinnertime. And countless are the addicts who increase their marijuana consumption as a way to cut down on another drug which has gotten out of hand. Over the long haul, control ploys fail. Using them, however, deceives one into thinking he is in control.

Seeking "Other" Help

With a family in turmoil, job performance deteriorating, alternating fits of depression and aggression, mounting debts, and a marriage "on the rocks" (pardon the expression), an alcoholic may realize he needs help of some kind. Eventually he does seek help, but not to stop drinking. In fact, if he goes to a doctor who confronts him about his drinking, he will find another doctor. Alcoholics have seen psychiatrists, counselors, surgeons, physicians, nurses, family therapists, psychologists, marriage counselors, priests, social workers, financial counselors, ministers, sex therapists and good friends looking for help to solve alcoholism's symptoms without addressing their cause.

Doctors find it easier to ask probing questions in search of a diagnosis of alcoholism if they perceive their inquiries as uncovering symptoms, and not as revealing shame. Sadly, however, health professionals in a position to help alcoholics either do not ask, do not know how to ask, or feel uncomfortable asking questions which will help an alcoholic focus on his problem. Regardless, the professional who does confront an addict ought to be prepared to deal with anger, denial and evasion. In the thick of his disease, an alcoholic does not want to be treated for it. He wants its consequences and its pain to go away.

Anxiety About Supply

Addicts worry about whether they bought enough, afraid they will run out. Drinking, drugging and getting the "stuff" become full time jobs. Three flakes of snow fall and alcoholics are off to liquor stores apprehensive about facing a coming blizzard without a stock.

After she had snorted a single line of cocaine, an addicted professional was certain she should have bought two grams instead of one. Bulk buying for addicts is not simply a matter of economics. The daily routine for one addict involved getting out of bed and spending the morning on the internet getting his supply. It was part of a schedule, part of his work day and work week.

From Middle to Late Stage: Having progressed through the middle stage of an addiction, even a headstrong alcoholic realizes he needs to slow down, stop for a while, or quit drinking altogether. When a period of self-imposed abstinence ends in unrelieved drinking (called a binge), addiction moves to its final stage. Once tolerance has developed, drinking after a dry spell picks up as if it had to make up for lost time, as if some preset drug level had to be regained. The appetite is ravenous.

Late Stage Symptoms: The word, "addict" comes from a Latin word which the Romans used when referring to the sentence given a *captured* enemy. Whoever chose it to describe drug dependence must have known addiction's final stage. At that stage an addict is a captive, and his symptoms are extreme. Drunkenness is frequent, outrageous, and rageful. At this stage, alcoholics may become homicidal or suicidal. Drunkenness is followed by abject guilt and shame. Attempts at control fail miserably. When dry, he is obsessed with alcohol. When drunk, he suffers miserably. At the end stage, an alcoholic no longer drinks for fun; he drinks to escape. Day in and day out he is depressed, guilt-ridden, drugged, agitated and withdrawing. Cycles of drinking and withdrawing are vicious. Health deteriorates. Medical emergencies crop up. Catastrophe is imminent.

The fears alcoholics experience at this stage are unreal, and bizarre. One alcoholic feared that his children would fall out of a window. When this fear was vivid he would grab his children even if they walked near a window. Another convinced himself that snakes had gotten into the plumbing of his house. It made going to the bathroom difficult. Such fears have been known to simply disappear with abstinence, but such an occurrence seems unlikely in their throes.

In the final stage, an alcoholic finds it hard to imagine living without alcohol. Some resign themselves to drinking. Others convince themselves they are not addicted, even after bouts of alcoholic hallucinosis. The layman is certain one would have to be crazy not to see the truth at this stage. Such reasoning is not far from the truth.

Cycles of Symptoms: Symptoms do not only follow each other in a string. Early symptoms precipitate later drinking. The two, symptoms and drinking, form a circle in which drinking relieves the symptoms which drinking has caused. Addiction breeds resentfulness, and resentments become an excuse to drink. Friday's drinking causes Saturday morning's irritability. Saturday evening's drinking soothes it. Drinking aims to relieve the very depression it has caused. Drinking drives friends away, and then alcohol fills the lonely void. Alcohol makes one nervous and sleepless, and then alcohol is used as tranquilizer and sleeping pill. The list goes on. The most obvious cycle in which a drug relieves the problem it has caused is withdrawal. But long before withdrawal, cycles of symptoms push addiction along its progressive course.

At What Point Sick? At some point it is no longer reasonable to think of a problem drinker as merely troubled; he is "sick." When Dr. Vaillant (1983, p. 44) says alcoholism *becomes* a disease when loss of control causes an individual's morbidity, what is meant is not that drinking alcohol makes someone dependent on it. He means that alcoholism is not called a "disease" until loss of control causes problems. But are alcoholics sick before drinking causes "recurring" problems? Can an adolescent be called sick with "addiction" before drinking completely wrecks his life?

Loss of control, that one after another chain of drinks, once established as a pattern, might be one point at which to call an alcoholic sick. But *loss of control* occurs so early in some cases that it seems premature to say that someone who has exhibited even repeated instances of *loss of control,* without other consequences, is as sick as someone who has lost his job and part of the functioning of his liver because of it. *Loss of control* occurs too early in some cases to claim that it is the "disease" stage.

There is another point which happens after *loss of control* but before morbid consequences, a point at which one's drug involvement is more serious than a mere habit and a potential problem. That point occurs when the drinking-symptom-drinking cycle meets *loss of control,* and both are denied. At that point, a drinker reaches a critical juncture in his history. His drinking self perpetuates, and it is unpredictable. And the drinker can see neither. At this point, a drinker cannot solve his problem because he does not believe he has one. *He is* the problem. He is trapped. He can only get worse. Add tolerance to this mix and resultant problems are virtually unavoidable. He may not seek treatment for his condition until it does cause recurring problems. However, when tolerance and *loss of control* are givens, when *drinking breeds drinking,* and when denial blocks one from seeing both, then morbid consequences are not merely probable, they are inevitable.

Whether addicts reach this point because of their brain's chemistry and its response to drugs; because they perceive drugs as pleasurable; or by some combination of chemistry, perception, and memory, addicts are sick from the moment *loss of control,* cyclic drinking and denial form a partnership.

The Dynamic Role of Enabling: Enabling is the other force which moves addiction along. Find an addict, and you will find four, five, six or more people who enable his addiction to continue. To remain active, an alcoholic must have help. He may need look no farther than his own living room, but he will need someone to help cover up the consequences of his drinking, deny that it is a problem, and patch up the troubles it causes. Those who badger him will find they provide him an excuse to drink when he runs out of his own excuses. Enabling takes the form of people, places, and things.

Enabling People: Because enabling serves a variety of purposes, family members are naturals for the job. They are close at hand and they have a vested interest. Quite understandably, husbands, wives, mothers, fathers, sons, and daughters end up enabling their alcoholic loved ones, believing all the while that they are doing the loving, the right, and even helpful thing to do.

One need not volunteer for the job of enabler to get it. If an enabler is not nearby, addicts seek them out. Some enablers play the role willingly, while others are suckered into it. Some addicts do enjoy "conning" others into enabling them, but not all addicts are con artists by inclination. Addiction coerces even the unwilling into manipulating others into being their enablers. Bosses, doctors, policemen, counselors, lawyers, neighbors and co-workers have been duped into it, unaware that they have been manipulated.

Circumstances as Enabling: Circumstances can enable an addict. A steady flow of cash helps a drugger to continue to use drugs. The one major difference between a rich addict and a poor one is that the rich one can afford to stay sick longer.

A job that does not require strict accounting of a worker's time and productivity helps an alcoholic get away with drinking without apparent problems. Businesses that sanction their employees drinking with clients, enable employees who are alcoholic. Alcoholic teachers get away with inadequate preparation and poor classroom performance. Lawyers, outside salesmen, and any worker who sets his own schedule can keep mornings free to recover from nights before. An alcoholic bartender is in heaven, as is a drug dependent pharmacist - both in the midst of a virtually limitless supply. Jobs do not cause alcoholism; they enable it.

Places, like neighborhoods, do not cause alcoholism. However, alcoholics and other addicts are drawn to certain places, neighborhoods and scenes because excessive drinking and drugging are permitted, common, or even expected there. For sure, certain vacation resorts are popular with alcoholics because they provide a no limits atmosphere in which to practice excess with impunity, as if the laws of the normal world were suspended at seaside resorts. Every city has neighborhoods which are not breeding grounds for addiction as much as they are places where addicts end up - places which attract and hold addicts because they supply, mask and enable addiction.

Put simply, enabling prolongs alcoholism by helping an alcoholic either delay hitting bottom or feeling it. Someone who is enabling can help an alcoholic just by stopping it.

Hitting Bottom: Believing an alcoholic must "hit bottom" before he recovers is a truth expressed in unfortunately extreme language. "Bottom" is imagined in such extreme ways that few addicts will last long enough to reach it in this life. Years ago alcoholics stayed sick longer than they had to. Today, intervention is the practice by which concerned others ban together with experts to cut short active addiction by presenting the addict a vivid picture of his condition and offering treatment for it. Contemporary thinking holds that since denial makes it difficult for an alcoholic to recognize that he has hit bottom, then someone will have to pick "bottom" up and hit him with it.

Bottom is not an event; it is not a situation; it is not a set of words; and it is not a physical condition. It is an awareness. An alcoholic hits bottom not when he says, "I am an alcoholic," not even when he considers his case a particularly bad one. Alcoholics do continue to drink long after both.

Denial keeps addicts from feeling the pain of their drinking and its consequences, and pain *is* part of hitting bottom. When denial erodes enough so that drinking hurts, then bottom is near. But pain itself is not bottom. Bottom happens when an addict utters one four-letter word, **"HELP."** Addiction humiliates its victim. Bottom occurs when it humbles him, when he becomes teachable, and when he asks for help. To ask for help means that one has to stop dictating the form that help takes. An alcoholic who asks for help but who then continues to make decisions contrary to the advice he is offered, who controls the source and course of his help is far from bottom. He is like the ocean voyager who is washed overboard and when thrown an orange life preserver asks for a choice of color. To hit bottom is to feel powerless. It is to ask for help unconditionally. It is surrender.

8

EARLY RECOVERY

By 1968, The American Medical Association had already defined alcoholism as an illness characterized by a "tendency to relapse" (p. 6). Recovery does not always begin the first time an alcoholic stops drinking. In early abstinence, the forces at work so characteristically retrigger drinking, or lead to other drug use, that early abstinence itself must be viewed as part of the active disease and integral to its process.

Designed to Destroy: Viewed anthropomorphically, addiction is intent on destroying its victim. It makes him sick. It tells him he's not sick. And then, after he does stop drinking, it makes him feel worse before he feels better.

It may seem silly to call alcoholism a killer because it makes one sick; lots of other diseases do that. Few, however, do as thorough a job, making an alcoholic sick in such a thorough way: physically, mentally, and emotionally. But unlike other diseases, denial prevents him from seeing that he is sick. The result is that he continues to drink and gets sicker. But there is more. Once he does stop, the shock of three withdrawals greets him: acute withdrawal, post-acute withdrawal, and a third withdrawal which might be called "psychological." He suffers emotional pain and has to handle it without resorting to drugs for relief. His problems seem overwhelming. His brain is stressed from years of abuse. And all of this sets him up to drink. And if he does drink, his disease resumes. He gets sicker than before, denies it more vigorously, and after several bouts of relapse, surrenders to the drug with greater despair than ever before. The simple truth is that some do not stay sober *through* early recovery precisely *because of* early recovery.

Three Withdrawals: Recovery confronts the novice with a series of shocks. First, there is acute withdrawal. This is a relatively brief period during which particular mood altering drugs, when stopped abruptly, cause a disturbing physical reaction in those who have become dependent on them. In cases of delirium tremens, alcohol withdrawal can be life threatening. Acute withdrawal is followed by a period during which a newly sober alcoholic continues at the mercy of a nervous system that has taken a beating for years and is likely to remain unstable for a time. This is post acute withdrawal. Finally, there is a series of shocks, described metaphorically as "psychological withdrawal." This three-part continuum constitutes early recovery. For a few, it is short-lived and comparatively mild. For many, it is intense and seems eternal. For some, it's a killer.

Acute Withdrawal: An addict who is dependent on a drug must maintain a level of that drug or a similar one if his nervous system is to remain stable. Should he stop his drug abruptly, he will experience a kind of "shock." When that shock is measurable, it is called "acute withdrawal." If his drug is a sedative (a downer), his withdrawal will take the form of a hyper-stimulated nervous system, causing vital signs, such as blood pressure, temperature, and pulse rate, to rise. If he has been using a stimulant drug (an upper), cocaine or amphetamine for example, withdrawal will take the form of a crash - with lethargy, fatigue, muscular aches and pains, and depression, sometimes severe enough to precipitate suicide (Schuckit, 1984a, pp. 97-98).

Withdrawal from alcohol begins within twenty-four hours after the last drink and peaks within two to three days, with measurable signs lasting four to five days (Schuckit, 1984a, pp. 74-75). Withdrawal from minor tranquilizers and barbiturates begins within twelve hours but may not fully emerge until the seventh day after abstinence, and some symptoms last for quite a long time (Schuckit, 1984a, pp. 34-36). Symptoms of sedative withdrawal run the spectrum from anxiety, restlessness, palpitations, hot and cold sweats, sleep disturbances and "shakes" to convulsions, hallucinations, and the most serious and a life-threatening complication of alcohol withdrawal, delirium tremens.

The cycle of "drug use - withdrawal - drug use" is easy to guess. The more an alcoholic drinks, the more intense his withdrawal. The more intense his withdrawal, the more he drinks to relieve it. And the more he drinks to relieve it, the more troublesome his withdrawal the next time he stops and the more he reacts in ways which cause even more stress.   Of course the more stressed he is, the more he drinks.

Withdrawal does not appear out of the blue. An alcoholic is not fine one day and in withdrawal the next. The insidiousness of withdrawal is that many contend with its subtler symptoms for months without knowing it. And since withdrawal invites the sufferer to take the very drug which produces it, alcoholics self medicate, using alcohol or a "freeze dried" substitute, like a tranquilizer, to soothe withdrawal symptoms.

In acute withdrawal, an alcoholic is neither a pleasant nor a welcome sight. And if the only time one has contact with him is when he is withdrawing, smelling of booze, arrogant, shaky and demanding, he seems entirely despicable, incredibly imperceptive - one of a stupid lot of people. Compassion is possible only if one has been privy to the long and fitful history that brought him to that point. Although admittedly, at that point, he is still not cuddly.

Post-Acute Withdrawal: Once acute withdrawal ends, the danger of convulsions and hallucinations, and even life-threatening complications is over. Withdrawal, however, does not end. There is a second period awaiting the new-comer, a period overcast with uncertainty and punctuated by sudden emotional storms. This is post acute withdrawal. It has not been well studied. Its causes and duration have yet to be defined with preci-sion. Thus, skeptics find it difficult to accept post acute withdrawal as anything more than the exaggeration of a stressed imagination. Recovering addicts, however, tell stories about early recovery. Since those stories are so similar and come from very different story tellers, post acute withdrawal seems more reasonably attributed to physical than psychological forces.

Unfortunately there is no data-supported answer to the question Al-Anon spouses most often ask, "How long does this damned early recovery stuff last?" Alcoholics Anonymous tells new members that they are too sick to make any major changes in their lives for a "year," but post acute withdrawal is rarely used as the name for that year. The advice most often passed on to A. A. newcomers is to "Keep coming back; it gets better." One of the hopes A. A. offers is that ear-ly recovery is endurable. Veterans laugh at how they agonized and analyzed during those days. To the rookie, however, it isn't funny.

Agitation and Restlessness

During acute withdrawal, an individual may experience so much motor restlessness and agitation he paces back and forth to relieve it. Even after acute withdrawal, he may feel agitated and restless for a while. This decreases in frequency and intensity over time.

Aches and Pains

Nonspecific aches and pains should not surprise someone who has been drinking heavily and steadily for years. He can expect them. If those aches and pains are specifically focused, severe, or persist and increase, a newcomer should consult a doctor who can figure out the cause and recommend a solution. However, he should seek a physician committed to avoiding mood-altering drugs for chemically dependent people. An alcoholic is responsible for his own recovery. He must take steps to insure that he does not deceive either himself or his physicians into thinking that he needs psychoactive drugs. An

A. A. friend or a sponsor can help him stay honest with himself. Self-honesty is not only critical throughout recovery, but especially in its early days.

Anxiety Attacks

Of the many post acute withdrawal problems, one of the most disconcerting is a sudden attack of anxiety. This is an anxiety which comes on for no apparent reason, or for reasons which are moderate compared to the anxiety they provoke. Anxiety prompts a newly recovering alcoholic to believe that tranquilizers are their remedy. So many of the problems of post acute withdrawal suggest mood altering drugs as their solution, that a newly recovering alcoholic can persuade even a well meaning physician into prescribing them, thus setting in motion either the development of an addiction to a second drug or a relapse back into his drug of choice. Numbers of alcoholics in early recovery have gotten started on a prescription addiction that way.

"Bad Chemistry Days"

Not a very scientific name but a very common experience, "bad chemistry days" are days when newly dry alcoholics awaken agitated. No sooner than he opens his eyes, he feels shaky, irritable, disturbed, and convinced something is sure to go wrong. Here's how one alcoholic expressed his bewilderment and frustration with the experience. "I figured something must be wrong with me. I'd wake up irritated even though nothing had yet happened. It was too damned early in the day for anything to have gone wrong, and yet I'd be agitated and ready to pick a fight."

The researcher who compiles a list of the types and duration of the "normal" problems of early recovery will do splendid service for recovering alcoholics who are comforted to learn when their problems are a familiar part of early recovery. If hard evidence backed that up, a newcomer could deal with early recovery problems with the assurance that certain problems are an expected part of getting well, and not a sign that he is getting worse. Such data would also provide treatment professionals with guidelines for determining when an individual's problems are beyond the expertise of self-help.

Diminished Concentration

A frustrating experience, especially for those whose jobs require attention to detail, is that powers of concentration are diminished in early recovery and remain so for a while.

Return of Dreaming

One surprise for those whose drug use has robbed them of normal sleep is that dreaming returns. Rebound dreaming is nearly always vivid and memorable. Some dreams are pleasant, some unsettling, and some are nightmares. Dreaming about drinking and drug use is not uncommon. Addicts dream about what they have loved and lost.

"Dry Drunks"

Though its exact cause is unknown, the "dry drunk" is a familiar phenomenon. "Dry drunk" means that the physical condition is "dry," but the behavior is *like* the behavior of a drunk (not literally staggering and slurring). The behavior is more like a drinker's emotions, which are demanding, moody, arrogant, agitated, and depressed. Dry drunks leave as quickly as they come, but they frighten family members who wonder whether drinking has resumed, adding another stress to already strained relationships.

Emotional Augmentation

The protracted withdrawal syndrome described by James Milam in *Under the Influence* includes increased emotional hypersensitivity (Milam & Ketcham, 1981, pp. 66-67, 97-98). The problem persists in early recovery. Emotional reactions exceed the stimuli which trigger them.

Flashes of Fear

Someone sober for the first time in years may experience spasms of fear, such as a child's fear of the dark or a brief fit of fear of driving. These attacks are not usually debilitating. They last usually only a short time and nearly everyone functions throughout, unsettling though they may be.

Fogged Thinking

Recovering addicts remain in a "fog" for a time, and nothing makes that clearer than coming out of it. Addiction progresses so gradually that it is like living in a world that has become overcast so gradually for so long that one forgets what the sun looks like. When the sun shines, it's a surprise.

Hypersensitivity and Self Consciousness

"Emotionally touchy" describes a newcomer. Along with emotional hypersensitivity comes painful self-consciousness. They make quite a lovely couple.

Memory Problems

Short-term memory deficits are part of early recovery. For some, the deficit is permanent, and individuals learn to compensate. Poor memory is exasperating and can be a source for anxiety about future functioning. An already sick mind finds it easy to rationalize poor memory as indicating a damaged brain and a hopeless recovery. Thinking like that easily provides an excuse to return to booze.

Itching

Itching during acute withdrawal, which old timers refer to as "whiskey fleas," plagues a few.

Mood Lability

Though not as extreme as the mood swings experienced by those with bipolar (manic-depressive) disorder, fluctuations of mood are part of early recovery. To someone who is sensitive to the novelty of feeling at all, mood swings seem intense, and newcomers think that medication may be needed to control them. But early recovery mood lability levels out with time. If mood swings persist or increase, an individual should consult a psychiatrist familiar with the differences between early recovery mood lability, bipolar mood swings, and depression's cycling.

Obsessive Ruminating

Ruminative thinking about trivial matters plagues early recovery for some. Addicts wonder if they have made some stupid mistake and find themselves checking and rechecking to prevent such mistakes. The thoughts are almost obsessive. One common obsessive thought, complicated by poor memory, is that something has been forgotten, left undone, or unattended.

Limited Attention Span

There is little wonder Alcoholics Anonymous publishes short, easy-to-read pamphlets available to the newcomer. Attention span and powers of concentration are limited.

Sleep Difficulties

A recovering alcoholic may not sleep normally for as many as five months after becoming abstinent. Many sleep fitfully. They fall asleep quickly but awaken in the middle of the night fully alert. Or they do not fall asleep until early morning and awaken an hour later fatigued. If sleep disturbances persist beyond five months or so, an alcoholic should consult a professional familiar with early recovery to determine if something else is causing a sleep problem. Other fairly common reasons alcoholics have trouble sleeping is that they consume too much caffeine and nicotine before bedtime. They also ruminate over unresolved shame, guilt and resentment. The biggest danger is that early recovery sleep problems will be treated with sleeping pills.

"Psychological" Withdrawal: After the first two withdrawals, there is a third which is no less troublesome and no less jeopardizing to sobriety. An alcoholic who stops drinking eliminates not only a drug which has kept his brain in balance, he stops a drug which provided activity, pleasure, companionship, structure and meaning. When the fog lifts, there is a third shock, a psychological one. Whether the problems of early recovery are caused by chemistry or psychology is academic. To the sufferer both are equally distressing.

Grief

Addicts love drugs. Even when they do not like the taste or the ambience which surrounds the drinking of it, alcoholics love the feeling – the zone - they get from alcohol.

Addiction is a lot like love. Love is blind; denial is a sort of blindness. Addicts have trouble believing drugs are his problem; lovers have trouble accepting their loved ones have faults. The analogy becomes apparent in recovery when an alcoholic spends his lunch hour in bars drinking tonic water and socializing with buddies. He is like the boy whose girl friend has dropped him but who drives past her house on his way home.

Because addiction is like love, recovery is like grief. This is similar to the feelings experienced by those who have lost a loved one (cf. Kubler-Ross, 1975, pp. 100-101). These are the feelings of *shock* - that one is alcoholic; *guilt* - about the past; *loneliness - a sense of isolation* - resulting from the loss of friends; *fear* - that one will not be able to handle the demands of recovery, and *anger and resentment* - about being alcoholic and having to deal with recovery. Ultimately, an alcoholic finds acceptance but not at the beginning.

Awakening to Consequences

To awaken from addiction is to awaken to its consequences, a lifetime of them: damage to health, injury to family, harm to career, havoc wreaked on self esteem and confidence, the erosion of structure and meaning in life. It's painful.

Continuing Struggles with Denial

Proficiency at self-deception does not vanish the day someone gets sober. After the first battle with denial, comes a second set of skirmishes. Alcoholics, sober a half-dozen months, wonder whether they are "really" alcoholic. "Did I really lose control? Could I have controlled my drinking if I had tried harder - *really* tried? I might have exaggerated my problem; I was in such bad shape I might have been vulnerable to thinking I had a problem when I didn't." For some alcoholics the only evidence which quiets such doubts is to experiment with "controlled" drinking. Unfortunately, some take long journeys back into drinking and/or drugging and denying. Some never return.

Drinking Dreams

Addicts who stop drugs dream about them. Alcoholics dream of drinking; nicotine addicts of smoking; cocaine addicts of snorting, and heroin addicts dream of injecting. The dreams are memorable and nearly always in Technicolor, but they are neither universally pleasant nor frightening. A Freudian interpretation is likely to regard such dreams as wish fulfillment or expression of subconscious anxiety. A simpler explanation is that the dreamer is an addict twenty-four hours a day, even as he sleeps.

Identity and Purpose of Life

After coming out of the fog, alcoholics, especially those who started drinking in their early teens, begin asking questions the fog has deferred, such as: "Who am I?"; "What do I enjoy?"; "How will I relax?"; "Am I shy?"; "How will I have fun?"; and "What's life about?" One newly recovering alcoholic expressed his early recovery philosophizing this way. "I sat in a mall on a Saturday afternoon watching people shop. I figured they were buying clothes for work the next week, all the while wondering why they were going to work next week. Was it so that they could make more money to come back next weekend to buy more clothes? Is that what non-alcoholics do with their lives?" Another alcoholic, one of many, discovered that he enjoyed certain forms of recreation simply because drinking was part of them. In recovery he didn't especially enjoy big league baseball and wasn't crazy about boisterous and deafening parties.

For non-addicts, it is difficult to appreciate the pleasure of intoxication and how central drinking can become for an alcoholic. When an alcoholic says drinking is the only thing he does for himself, it is only barely overstatement. In fact, as dependency worsens, even alcoholics who used to enjoy their jobs find that their attitudes change. The job provides little satisfaction in itself. It is a means to an end. That end is to drink. And so to lose drinking is to lose one's reason for working. Thus, it is not surprising sober alcoholics begin to wonder if they should change jobs or start new careers.

Inhibition and Self Consciousness

A. A. members sooner or later recognize that they waste part of every A. A. meeting rehearsing what to say if called on. Drunks get lots of practice spouting insights in uninhibited free form style when they are loaded, but they have had little practice telling what they think and feel when they are sober. Recovery is a self-conscious time. When alcohol or other drugs have been part of sex, sober lovemaking is awkward and embarrassing, clumsy and inept, and, for a few, impossible for a time. One of the quickest roads back to drinking is paved with the thought that sobriety means no more of the joy of sex.

The Shock of Feelings

For an addict who has not weathered an emotional experience without a drug, sober feelings hit with a jolt. Mild feelings seem strong, powerful feelings astonish, and augmented ones overwhelm. In early recovery, feelings are accompanied by two messages: 1) feelings are overwhelming; and 2) they are everlasting. They seem remorseless and relentless. Guilt, anger, anxiety, resentment, fear, sadness, hurt, shame and loneliness come in extra helpings, and they come augmented and intensified. Even love, peace and happiness feel peculiar. For an emotional beginner, joy seems strange, and it may bring tears. Alcoholism never taught anyone to feel normally.

The Insidiousness of Early Recovery: Early recovery is crammed with ironies. Alcoholism takes away the ability to deal with stress and then gives one more stress to deal with. Alcohol blurs reality, and reality comes blaring back in recovery. This is a reality made more painful than it is for others because of addiction, and a reality that must be endured without chemical relief or tranquilizers. Alcoholism robs one of the opportunities to learn about feelings, and then dishes up extra helpings of feelings to be experienced undrugged for the first time in years, and these feelings are intensified by an agitated nervous system. As the meaning of "never drinking again" is beginning to dawn on him, the world seems intent on reminding him that "weekends are made for Michelob."

Getting Through Early Recovery: If there is a goal for early recovery, it is to get through it. How? Any way that works! The object? To save your ass. Faced with the question of how one will save his life, there ought to be little interest in programs aimed at achieving personal potential through intellectual stimulation and emotional discovery.

The objective is to abstain.

The motive is to stay alive.

And the method is any one that will work.

The wisest move an alcoholic or other addict can make is to go to Alcoholics or Narcotics Anonymous, and the reasons are simple. It's free; it's available, and it works. Faced with nearly any other problem, no one will choose a solution which is expensive, hard to access and unreliable. They pick something that is inexpensive, dependable, and available. And yet, when alcoholism is the problem and Alcoholics Anonymous is the recommended solution, otherwise sane people ask if there isn't another way. The reason for so perverse a stance reduces most often to two deeply human truths: pride and denial. To go to Alcoholics Anonymous is to admit *you need help to stop drinking*. After all, only *real* alcoholics go to A. A.

The newcomer who goes to A. A. finds people whose interest is to stay sober and help others do the same - people who accomplish the former by the latter. When he finds sober A. A. members, he finds no critics, no judges and no experts. He hears no mandates, rules, regulations, or edicts. He sees no bosses, no chain of command and no organizational superstructure. He meets people. Some are pleasant and some unpleasant, some young and some old, some preachy and some tolerant, some brilliant and some not, some shy, some talkative, some extroverted, some like him and others not, and some who are sicker than others. He finds people helping each other.

9

ADDICTION

Learning about addiction is impossible if one presumes that versions on television and in the movies are typical of it. Most addicts live lives that are not as exciting as prime time would lead us to believe. Some live dangerously, of course, but most suffer with less excitement than the big screen shows. Even though alcoholics are drug addicts, rarely is that word used to describe them. Kids think that marijuana is not addictive because they think it does not cause withdrawal. The word addiction itself has been stretched to refer to so many things (like compulsive work, computer gaming, sex, gambling, overeating, bulimia, house cleaning, nail-biting, and insane drug use), that the English Language runs the risk of losing any communicable meaning for the word because of that stretching.

Addiction is used here to refer to a pattern of alcohol and other drug use. Other behaviors do resemble drug and alcohol addiction, and sometimes strikingly so. But there are enough differences among drug addiction, compulsive gambling, drug use, and sex that this book sidesteps that interesting issue for the time being.

Learning about drug addiction often involves unlearning myths and misleading preconceptions about it.

Extreme Images: A young woman who used every drug available to her on the streets and many found in pharmacies, who put those drugs into her body by nearly every orifice available, still refused to call herself a drug addict because she never injected heroin. To her, injecting heroin was real addiction, and like so many addicts, she preferred to think of addiction as that particular extreme behavior because she hadn't done that. It helped her deny she had the problem.

For several reasons, not the least of which is their failure to perceive alcohol as a drug, alcoholics do not regard themselves as drug addicts. Crystal decanters and cocktail shakers have been popular drug paraphernalia in this country for a lot longer than pot bongs and coke spoons, and yet alcoholics use "addict" to refer to the "hard core." Even "hard core" when it refers to heroin addicts, reflects a use of language with little basis in either logic or common sense. By any criteria for determining how dangerous a drug happens to be, alcohol should be considered more troublesome than heroin. Alcohol is particularly toxic and withdrawal from it can be life-threatening, whereas heroin withdrawal, though prolonged and painful, is not. Heroin addicts die in withdrawal but not from of it. They die from overdosing; they commit suicide; they are murdered; or they die in accidents. They do not die, however, as the direct medical consequence of withdrawing from heroin. As consequences go, death from alcohol withdrawal seems more profound than diarrhea from heroin withdrawal. And yet heroin is called the "hard" drug, and alcohol, if called a drug at all, is a "soft" one.

Old ideas die hard. Americans equate addiction with particular drugs and particular means of using them along with two other notions that persist, despite that neither is true. The first is that physical withdrawal is the heart of addiction. Addiction and physical dependence are considered to be the same thing, and so people believe that someone is not addicted until he or she ends up with the shakes. The second notion, also false, is at the opposite end of the spectrum. It is the belief that addiction is psychogenic. In other words, psychological forces are the ones that drive individuals to drink and drug until they end up needing drugs to keep from falling apart. And the corollary of this already mistaken notion is that the weakness of character which causes addiction also explains why addicts relapse after they have quit. The erroneous notion is that irresponsibility causes addiction, and weakness keeps addicts addicted. The notion is neat but just too simplistic. Any time a phenomenon involves two things as complex as the human brain and psychoactive drugs, that phenomenon is not going to be as simple as "it is all in your mind."

Proneness to Addiction: Multiple Forces: To think of addiction as purely psychological is a mistake. To think of it as purely biochemical is yet another mistake. Neither of those forces alone explains why rational human beings, some with commendable control in other areas of their lives, persist in using drugs even after it is clear that drugs are killing them. If nothing else, becoming addicted is not simple.

In order to persevere in using immoderate amounts of drugs, one must have a nervous system which permits such use, a brain that responds in some special or unusual ways to drugs. An individual must also be able to tolerate high doses of drugs if he is to become addicted to them. He must get enough pleasure from drugs that the risk of using them seems worth it. It's complex.

It should be obvious that those who get great pleasure from drugs are more susceptible than those who do not. If the former tolerates high doses, his susceptibility doubles, and the latter is protected both by his lack of response and his lack of tolerance. If one person experiences drinking as relaxing, another finds it stimulating, and a third enjoys both the "Wee!" and the "Ah!" all three will be susceptible. However, the lure the drug holds for the third is twofold. And if that third person finds that by increasing the dose of the drug he increases its pleasure, and if he finds that he has no protective reaction against high doses, he will be saddled with several times the susceptibility of the others. If human beings behave like lab animals, research into tetrahydroisoquinolines (THIQ) might explain why those who produce high levels of acetaldehyde when drinking might drink in compulsive ways and become dependent on drugs, as appears to be the case with experimental animals injected with these THIQs (cf. Myers and Melchior, 1977).

Dr. Mark Schuckit (1980), in an article nearly everyone will understand, summarizes the mechanisms which explain problem drinking.

The point is this. In order to become an addict, one must have more than a mind to. He must have a nervous system susceptible to addiction, and this involves more than simply using too much of a drug for too long. What seems certain is that the locus of addiction is to be found not in the mind but in the brain. It is virtually impossible to find any research today that focuses on the psychology of proneness to addiction. In fact, Dr. Erickson's recent work, *The Science of Addiction* (2007) summarizes in its third chapter, a range of theories to explain chemical dependence. The lay reader with the patience to study it is well advised to read that book. Each of the theories discussed there involves brains, not minds.

In "Addiction, a Disease of Compulsion and Drive: Involvement of the Orbitofrontal Cortex," Dr. Nora Volkow postulates that multiple factors, "both conscious (craving, loss of control, drug preoccupation) and unconscious processes (conditioned expectation, compulsivity, impulsivity, obsessiveness)" and that the brain's reward circuits, as well as circuits involved with compulsive behaviors, are at work in the addictive person (Volkow & Fowler, 2000). It makes sense that addiction is not the result of a single event and a single brain system, but that a chain of brain and behavioral events in multiple brain systems leads to a "cycle of spiralling dysregulation of brain reward systems that progressively increases, resulting in compulsive drug use and loss of control over drug taking." (Koob & Le Moal, 1997) The process is likely to be complex.

Research today converges on the conclusion that no single path to addiction is likely to explain vulnerability to addiction, its progressive nature, and susceptibility to relapse. A cluster of biochemical, as well as environmental and psychological, propensities explains why one person is prone and another protected (cf. Edenburg, 2003), (Koob & Bloom, 1988), (Koob & Le Moal, 1997), (Volkow& Fowler, 2000), (Volkow et al., 2006).

The brain's complex response to drugs is not the only prerequisite for addiction. And, even though a potential addict must be a person with more than just a mind to become one, he must at least have a mind that relishes in the pleasure of drinking, enjoys the energizing effect of drugs, and sees drinking and/or drug use as somehow appropriate to his personality and lifestyle. To become addicted, a person must be enamored with drugs enough so as to slip all the more readily into denying difficulties which result from using them. Without both the brain of an addict and the mind of one, a person either gets no kick from drugs or doesn't consider what he does get a big deal.

Protection Against Addiction: Children of alcoholics have endured living with an addicted parent. And if anyone has powerful motivation to avoid addiction, it would be those who have lived with it and suffered because of it. Scientific evidence, adoption and twin studies, however, show us that children of alcoholics do not seem protected by that motivation. In fact, not only does such motivation fail to protect them, as a group, children of addicts are more prone to developing the problem than others. The human mind may provide additional protection to someone who hopes to avoid addiction, but by itself, psychic protection may not be enough. The power of the mind might need help from a protective brain.

Anyone who becomes sick, groggy, or dizzy from just a couple of doses of a drug is not a likely candidate for a drug addiction. The person who falls asleep from a second drink is not very likely to have a third. If one person finds a particular drug a mellow experience, another finds the same drug energizing, and a third finds it agitating, the first two are prone for different reasons, while the third is protected against excessive doses. Those who like the peace that sedatives provide are more susceptible to sedatives than those who get groggy when using them. Obviously individuals who find stimulant drugs energizing will be drawn to them more than those who find stimulants agitating.

High levels of dopamine, the brain's reward pathway, may protect human beings from becoming alcoholic. It may even protect those with a family history of alcoholism who are susceptible because of genetic factors. The current Director of The National Institute for Drug Abuse (NIDA), Dr. Nora Volkow, collaborated in research in which rats, both those trained to drink alcohol as well as those with a genetic predisposition for drinking, reduce their alcohol intake if the level of dopamine in their brains increases (Thanos et al., 2001), (Thanos et al., 2004). Complementing her work with animals, Dr Volkow has found that high levels of dopamine receptors (D_2) may provide protection against addiction even in people with a history of family alcoholism. Her words express the study's outcome succinctly, "The finding of high D_2 receptor availability in subjects who are not alcoholic, despite risk of alcoholism due to family history, supports the hypothesis that high D_2 receptor levels exert a protective effect against alcoholism" (Volkow et al., 2006, p. 1006).

These findings are consistent with similar results of a study of siblings discordant for cocaine abuse, presented at the 42nd Annual Meeting of the American College of Neuropsychopharmacology, "that showed not only that cocaine-abusing siblings had a lower D_2 receptor level than a control group, but also that the non-abusing sibling had a higher D_2 receptor level than the control group" (Volkow et al., 2006, p. 1004). The lower the D_2 receptor levels the more cocaine abuse. The higher the D_2 level the less cocaine abuse. Dr. Volkow cautions that this study is not the whole story and factors of genetic susceptibility, personality, and environment are likely to play roles in proneness to alcoholism (Volkow et al., 2006).

Addiction doesn't come in one level of severity and intensity. Some people are diagnosable at age sixteen; others are not in treatment until they are sixty. There are addicts with severe symptoms and multiple blackouts that are prolonged and frightening. Others have mostly social consequences. Health problems are the major consequence for a few. While some people drink heavily without apparent impact on health, others suffer serious physical health consequences from lesser amounts. There are both heavy drinkers who do not develop alcoholism and others who do, even though they drink lesser amounts. Not all children of alcoholics develop alcoholism. Some do, whereas others born of the very same parents do not. What makes most sense of this variety is that proneness, as well as protection, works at multiple levels.

Proneness and Protection: Some people seem to come with only proneness; others with nothing but protection. What is most probable is that the majority of people come with a combination of proneness and protection, explaining why some cases are of earlier onset and more flagrant than others. Here is a list in laymen's terms of the variety of those factors.

Proneness Factors	Protection Factors
Rapid Cellular Adaptation to a Drug	Immediate Dysphoric Effect
Early High Tolerance	Painful Next Day After-Effect
Dramatic Euphoric Response	Sensitivity to Rising BAL*
Missing Protection against a Toxin	Early Toxic Response to a Drug
Risk Taker	Conservative Mind Set
Too few Dopamine Receptors	Protective Dopamine Receptors
	*BAL – Blood Alcohol Level

Potential addicts may be those who have brains that quickly adapt to drugs, brains whose functioning changes even from their earliest exposure to drugs. Other people discover as they mature that they were never really crazy about how drugged alcohol made them feel. Conservative folks are less likely to try a risky drug than risk takers. Most adults remember high school friends who could hold their booze and others who couldn't from the start. Hangovers are mild or severe for different people. Some drinkers find that the more they drink the better they feel. Others find the opposite – more feels worse. Some people love booze. Others like it. Some can take it or leave it.

Still a Mystery: Addiction's exact cause or causes remain a mystery. And, although research is hot on the trail of labeling dopamine (the brain's pleasure center) as the center of susceptibility and protection, we still do not know yet whether those who are susceptible are born with both the brain and the mind which are its ingredients, or whether they are born with its chemistry and develop its thinking only after exposure to drugs, or the reverse. How much of the way the mind thinks is connected to the way the brain functions? We are still not sure precisely how many susceptibility ingredients there happen to be. Definitions, therefore, tend to describe addiction rather than cite its causes. What we do know about addiction is analogous to what we know about a magnetic field. It exists. It is powerful. It is predictable. It is describable. But what it is, we're not sure.

What Addiction Is Not: Addictive drug use is clarified by contrasting it to other ways of using drugs which are not in the nature of addiction. Drug taking may be described by any of the following:

Drug Use. Nearly everyone has taken a prescription drug at one time or another. Many Americans drink alcohol, and more than a few use "recreational" drugs. "Use" describes drug taking which causes no harm, no problems.

Drug Abuse - Drug abuse is use that is harmful, risky or dangerous. Drug abuse is problematic, but it is not addiction. Not everyone who drinks too much once in a great while is rightly characterized as an "abuser" either. Abuse describes a behavior – harm. Abuser is the word we use when someone characteristically gets into trouble or is harmed by his use. In addition, not everyone who is a drug abuser is, therefore, a drug addict.

Drug Reliance. To avoid the confusion when the word "dependence" is used to describe both a physical and a psychological condition, the word "reliance" describes those people who consistently count on drinking or drug taking to change how they feel. Provided the user is not tolerant of drugs, does not lose control, and causes no harm to himself or others when he drinks, someone who counts on booze or pot to change how he feels might be called alcohol *reliant*.

Drug Dependence. Dependence describes the physical state characterized by withdrawal when an individual abruptly stops using a drug. Dependence, in other words, is used here to mean physical dependence, not psychological dependence.

Addiction. Addiction is unusual involvement with a drug. It is not identical to physical dependence. Though an addiction may include one's becoming physically dependent, we need not wait until someone becomes dependent to call him an addict. An addict is that person who tries to control his drinking and/or drugging, but fails. Addicts differ from those who are drug reliant because both tolerance and loss of control characterize addictive use. Addiction exists without physical dependence. Physical dependence exists sometimes without addiction. Sometimes both exist in the same person, but addiction and dependence are not the same thing.

Dependence and Addiction: Most people make the mistake of thinking that addiction is physical dependence, and that the words are synonymous. It is an axiom of language that whenever two words describe exactly the same thing, one of those words will disappear eventually from the living language. This has not yet happened to "addiction" and "dependence." And it is not likely to happen because there is a clear difference between them, which is illustrated from hypothetical as well as actual cases.

If a patient is given narcotics to relieve the pain of surgery, he will become dependent on narcotics if they are administered long enough - a short time actually. The patient will be unable to stop taking the drug without going into withdrawal. But how should we describe this patient, if once he is withdrawn, he never seeks and never uses narcotics or any other drug again? Consider how different he is from the person who became dependent on narcotics for the same reason, but who does pursue drugs and continues to use them after he has been withdrawn from them. Both have at one time been physically dependent on a narcotic, but only one persisted in using the drug. Does it make sense to call both "drug addicts?" It is unlikely that every soldier who was given morphine to relieve the pain of battle wounds returned to the States to become a junkie. Some did. Others did not. It blurs the differences between them to consider both addicts just because they were both physically dependent at one point in their lives. Such use of language serves neither linguists nor health professionals.

A patient was admitted to the hospital after prolonged use of a narcotic drug prescribed to help control a serious health problem. The prescription led to his becoming physically dependent and unable to function because of the dose he needed. On his first day of hospitalization, he asked the doctors how quickly he could be withdrawn from the narcotic drug. Addicts do not ask such questions on day one; they are more likely at the start to tell doctors the dose they need to remain stable. After the first few days of his stay, this patient asked again if his detoxification could be speeded up; he was tired of feeling drugged. Addicts don't think like that. Even addicts who are motivated to detoxify still want their "coming down" to be a gradual and soft landing. This patient was clearly physically dependent. To call him a drug addict would only mislead others about his actual behavior.

The current *Diagnostic and Statistical Manual, DSM IV* (American Psychiatric Association [APA], 1994) defines "Substance Dependence," the highest degree of a substance problem, without requiring physical withdrawal as part of that diagnosis. The conclusion one might infer is that physical dependence is not an addict's most serious problem, and it isn't. When viewed from the perspective of which is more serious, physical dependence or addiction's psychological drive, it becomes apparent that physical dependence is distressing and painful, but is resolved in a short time with little psychic effort on the sufferer's part. An addict's memory of the pleasure and the thrill and comfort of intoxication, however, may take years and a major effort to overcome.

Besides, addiction proves no less fatal without withdrawal. A nineteen-year-old had been found guilty of driving while intoxicated several times. His driver's license was revoked. His tolerance was high. He attended A. A. meetings on and off for a year, and he did want to stop drinking. One night he died while driving drunk. Though he never suffered withdrawal when he stopped drinking, his drive for alcohol - his addiction to it - proved no less fatal. Physical dependence complicates addiction, and that complication is serious indeed for some. But addiction is complicated enough even without the shakes.

Use and Addiction: Addiction is obviously not simply drug use, but an explanation of "use" helps to clarify addiction by contrast. Drugs are used in two ways: by prescription and as recreation - for health and for fun. Which drugs should be accepted as social or recreational, and which not, spark heated debate in almost any gathering. One group accepts marijuana as recreational; another does not. Cocaine is considered more dangerous today than it was in the late 1980s. At that time, there were "jet-setters" who considered it a form of recreational drug use (and some still do). The debate about which drugs ought to be considered socially acceptable is likely to persist, and yet debaters might agree on what constitutes social use even though they continue to disagree about to which drugs the criteria ought to apply.

Social-Recreational Use

Social drug use may be interpolated from social drinking, and social drinking differs from addictive drinking in several ways. Social drinkers use alcohol socially and sociably. They drink on social occasions and act in socially acceptable ways. Their drinking is moderate and limited. Most important of all, alcohol causes no problems. It is not the social drinker's pattern to insult his brain with toxic doses. Intoxication is possible, but atypical. The social user is not stoned, sloshed, wasted, or smashed on a regular basis. He may get drunk on a New Year's Eve, and he may even intend to get drunk, but drunk is not his style. For him serious intoxication is rare. His ordinary pattern is to have a few drinks over several hours, feel mildly euphoric, have coffee, and go home. He does not arrive at parties half lit, gulp down several drinks, get loud and thick-tongued, belt down one for the road, and top the evening off with a nightcap before passing out. He doesn't smoke a joint when he gets home.

Prescription Drug Use

A drug which is recommended by a licensed physician for a health purpose is called prescription use. It is prescription use only as long as it is the physician, not the patient, who determines the drug's dose, frequency and route of administration. Only the physician prescribes changes in those directions. Prescription use is not meant to be harmful. The treating physician manages harmful side effects and stops the drug if necessary. Finally a prescription drug is discontinued when health returns. Taking pills from a friend is not prescription use. To party with pills, to self prescribe, or to double the recommended dose is not legitimate prescription use. To save pills to be taken all at once is not using them as prescribed. And it can hardly be called legitimate prescription use to continue taking a drug fifteen years after one has regained his health.

Abuse and Addiction: The line between drug use and drug abuse is crossed when drug use causes harm. Drug abuse is quite simply any use that causes problems of any kind, either physical or psychological. There is abuse, and there are abusers. The one describes an isolated behavior; the other describes a characteristic pattern of behavior.

The line that separates "Drug Abuse" from "Drug Addiction" is more difficult to draw. Criteria for Drug Abuse in the *Diagnostic Manual (DSM IV)* (APA, 1994) rely on one's persistence in taking drugs despite recurrent problems caused by them. However, it is precisely that "persistence" which suggests a more serious problem than "abuse" suggests. "Problems" distinguish "Use" from "Abuse." What in part distinguishes Abuse from Addiction is "persistence" despite those problems. Drinking enters a special realm when one keeps doing something which harms him. Abusers and addicts may drink equal amounts, but it is not the amount which makes one an addict. It is his persistence after he has lost job, family, self-respect and health, which marks the difference between him and an abuser as qualitative. Prudence, common sense, reason, and will power do not have nearly as strong a clutch on a person as does his drug.

Addictive Drugs? Are some drugs abusable and others not? Are some drugs merely abusable and others addictive? Are there two separate categories for drugs? Only when the criterion for addiction requires evidence of measurable physical dependence will the list of addictive drugs differ from the list of abusable ones. Any drug can be abused, but the drugs with the highest potential for abuse are those that affect the brain in a way perceived as desirable or pleasurable. Such drugs generally fall into the category of mood altering drugs such as depressants, stimulants, and hallucinogens. A drug is an addictive drug if, besides producing pleasure, tolerance for the drug develops. Drugs capable of causing withdrawal may be addictive, but they are not addictive because of withdrawal. They are addictive because they are pleasurable, because tolerance for them develops, and because addicts feel "called" by them long after they have withdrawn.

Is marijuana addictive? A committed member of a self help group had remained abstinent from alcohol and cocaine for more than eight years. "Alcohol made me sick and cocaine threw me around the room" was his way of describing his addiction to those drugs. The drug he struggled to quit, and unsuccessfully so for those eight years, was marijuana. "I would find myself hiding in my back yard, ashamed my wife would find me smoking pot; it was driving me crazy." It took nearly two years of counseling before he felt comfortable and safe without marijuana.

Only those who believe a drug must cause profound withdrawal, as is the case with alcohol, insist that marijuana is not an addictive drug. Marijuana is pleasurable. Tolerance for it does, in fact, develop. And some of its users find marijuana nearly impossible to stop. For those reasons marijuana is as addictive as alcohol, opiates, stimulants, tranquilizers, cocaine, barbiturates and nicotine. In the drama of addiction the drug is but one member of the cast. The complete program includes a list of addiction prone people as well as a list of drugs that have certain powers and characteristics. Both lists are likely to prove complex.

Some drugs are more seductive than others, and more problematic because of it. How troublesome a particular drug is may be measured by the extent to which it matches five criteria:

- The drug hits you quick.
- It takes you high.
- It leaves you fast.

- It is thought to be safe.
- It comes with potent cravings.

Cocaine, if snorted, produces its euphoric effects within a minute, and if injected almost immediately. Cocaine is a seductive drug because there is an immediate reward for the user.

How high does it take you? Heroin is a narcotic that renders users out of it. Another narcotic, Methadone, allows users to function because it doesn't take the user so high.

How fast does the drug leave you? A drug, such as cocaine – crack whose effects dissipate within less than an hour is a seductive drug for two reasons. Any drug that dissipates rapidly is perceived to be a low risk experience, after all a cocaine snorter sees his high as lasting less than twenty minutes. To the contrary, although there are addicts who prefer hallucinogens, that drug's effects may last for an uncomfortably long time. The other reason a drug like cocaine is troublesome is that since the effects dissipate so rapidly the user has to dose more frequently in order to sustain his high.

How safe is the drug thought to be? This is not the same as "How safe is the drug?" A drug thought to involve serious risk will be avoided a lot longer than one that users think involves little risk. The history of drug popularity is an interesting story of drugs that come in and out of favor, because at one time a drug is considered safe and at another time the same drug is thought to be quite dangerous. LSD has had such a history; cocaine too.

How much craving does use of the drug produce? Nicotine is particularly troublesome because craving for nicotine is persistent and intense. Crack addicts claim cravings for that drug are overwhelming.

Reliance and Addiction: By definition, mood altering drugs alter moods. Although human beings are born with natural ways of changing the way they feel, people seem eager to find easier and quicker ways of doing anything. At some time or another, a majority of Americans take a drink to relax.

When alcohol or another drug consistently serves that purpose, such use becomes life limiting at the very least. And such a user might be called alcohol or drug reliant. If a person's drug use is not marked by tolerance, causes no problems, and is consistently under his or her control (he sets a modest limit and sticks to it), reliance might adequately describe the person who regularly and near-exclusively drinks to relax. A tolerant drinker who loses control and who has problems because of drinking is best described by another word. His drug involvement is more complicated.

In the literature of chemical dependency "Reliance" is not used widely to describe a form of drug taking, and the term might prove more useful in a hypothetical rather than statistical way since the numbers of those who are drug reliant and not already abusers or addicts may be quite small. There is also a risk that a word, such as "reliance," creates a category that addicts will seize on to describe their own use when it is obvious they are addicted. Never the less "reliance" does provide a useful way to describe a schizophrenic's drinking or his smoking marijuana when that use aims at relieving psychotic symptoms. If the schizophrenic patient does not lose control, is not tolerant, and if his use causes no problems, then he might be said to be "relying" on a drug.

Self medication is one form of Reliance, but there are other forms of Reliance that are not properly called self medication. Reliance might also describe the drug use of a few teenagers (perhaps very few) who drink or smoke pot at parties as a way of dealing with shyness, self consciousness and inhibition, provided, of course, those teenagers are not tolerant, do not lose control, and have no recurrent problems because of drug use. In other words, teenagers who are not already drug abusers or drug addicts might be called alcohol or marijuana reliant, and in need of counseling because of it. Someone who regularly deals with stress by drinking or smoking marijuana might be called Reliant, provided he does not already satisfy criteria for addiction or abuse.

To rely on drugs as a way of dealing with life's stresses is not healthy, and both adults and young people are well advised to find natural ways to alter their moods before relying on drugs to do so. But reliance on a drug is not addiction to a drug. The drive which pushes addicts goes far beyond their counting on drugs to change the way they feel. That drive is progressive, time-consuming, pre-occupying, overwhelming, and increasingly obsessional, even after the drug has "stopped working." Drugs are not merely a means to reward success or relieve inhibition for addicts. They are central. Non-addicts can take it or leave it. Addicts claim they can, but they don't.

Progressive Signs of Addiction: Severe addiction does not develop instantly, without warning. Signs foreshadow it; those signs include:

- Growing desire for the pleasure, joy or relief of drugs.
- Willingness to experiment with improving the "high."
- Willingness to spend increasing amounts of money for drugs.
- Tendency to maximize the pleasure and minimize the pain of one's drug use.
- Tendency for drinking and/or drug use to dominate conversation.
- Growing tendency to rely on drugs for relief.
- Neglect of past interests and hobbies.
- Increasing value placed on paraphernalia.
- Tendency to decline invitation where alcohol or other drugs will not be available.
- Tendency to choose drinking over other recreational alternatives.
- Forgetfulness of the interests, agenda and activities agenda of family members.
- Difficulty limiting drug use to appropriate times and places.
- Self consciousness about use.

- Perception that sober time is boring, and high time brief.
- Tendency to hurry through one's routine to get to drinking.
- Continued use though prudence, common sense and past experience indicate it is unsafe.
- Tendency to choose companions and environments which mask use and intoxication.
- Tendency to rearrange schedules to suit use.
- Drifting toward a lifestyle which suits one's drug use.
- Tendency to avoid non-users and gravitate to users.
- Tendency to discount behavior under the influence.
- Tendency to ridicule sober or "straight" people.
- Tendency to associate drinking and drugging with even routine activities.
- Tendency to sacrifice values, principles and ideals for the sake of the drug.
- Preoccupation with past use and attempts to recapture it.
- Growing preoccupation with the next use.
- Deciding to end a personal relationship rather than stop.
- Growing need to justify frequency and/or amount.
- Irritability with those who question use.
- Drinking and drugging to feel normal.
- Neglect of health, grooming and routine self caring.
- Irritability when frustrated from use.
- Continuing use after it has created or exacerbated health, job, family, school, and legal problems.
- Neglect of family and responsibilities.
- Anxiety while purchasing the drug.
- Pleasure without drugs becomes difficult.
- Personal and family property sold to finance use.

- Anxiety about running out.

- Irritability and depression when not using.

- Growing undefined fears and free floating anxiety.

- Resigning oneself to reduced personal, moral, social and ethical standards because of use.

- Tendency to take risks either to get drugs or while under their influence.

- Fear of insanity.

- Inability to stop without help.

Addiction: An addict is tolerant of drugs, loses control of their use, and is unable to abstain or to limit his use after repeated attempts or despite a desire to do so, or who persists in using drugs despite harm or problems caused by them. To qualify as an addict one need not suffer withdrawal. Tolerance, loss of control, and persistence, however, are essential to the diagnosis.

Tolerance and loss of control are problems all by themselves. If one were to develop drug tolerance without manifesting any other sign of a drug problem, his tolerance alone would be a problem of some magnitude. The tolerant drinker has no choice but to drink in harmful amounts in order to get what drinking has to offer. To feel the high he must suffer harm. A tolerant alcoholic faces a dilemma not unlike the cancer patient who has become tolerant of painkillers. Painkillers may cause as much dysfunction as pain. And so, even if tolerance is not currently causing a problem, tolerance can quite readily become the cause of future problems, at the very least health problems. Tolerance, therefore, is a problem.

That loss of control is problematic is obvious. Someone who cannot predict how much he will drink, for how long, and what will happen as a result, has undeniably a drinking problem. His drinking is unpredictable – it may be life-threatening, and that is a problem.

Those who are tolerant and who lose control have built-in problems and should want to stop for those two reasons. If they can stop and do so without a lot of "sturm and drang," who is to say they are addicted? For addicts, stopping is tough. They try but fail. They succeed for a time, but eventually they pick up again. When an addict does manage to stop, it is with a struggle - a psychological struggle. He cuts down, but eventually he goes back to, and surpasses, old levels. With strong motivation, under pressure, or with a stable external structure, alcoholics have quit drinking for periods of time. But sooner or later, they pick up and are out of control again and worse than before. An alcoholic who is strongly motivated might even manage to drink without getting drunk for a time. But eventually he does get drunk, and it happens often at the worst time and with worse results. That an alcoholic is never able to stop, and that addictive drinking is one long and continuous affair, is a myth. The truth is that before the final stage most alcoholics can stop for a while when they want to. Their problem is that they have little desire to do so, and when they do, it doesn't last long.

Addiction does not have a single face. An addict may experience mild or severe problems. Addiction might hit someone in the mainstream of society or those in a counter-culture. An addiction may be riddled with illegal activity, or it may involve not a single illegal act. It may be longstanding or of recent onset. Cravings may be mild or intense. Addiction may be complicated by physical dependence with severe withdrawal symptoms, or it may be withdrawal-free. A motivating secondary gain, financial profit for instance, may keep one addict using longer than another who gets only wasted from his addiction. There is, after all, more than one way to get loaded from addiction. Such considerations may help treatment teams determine the type of interventions appropriate for particular patients, but they are not addiction itself. Addiction happens to cigarette smokers and heroin mainliners, to drinkers and speed freaks, and to cocaine snorters and prescription drug users.

Cycles of Addiction: In *I'll Quit Tomorrow*, Vernon Johnson describes alcoholism as developing in phases, starting with a learning phase and ending in harmful dependency (Johnson, 1973, pp. 16-34). Addiction involves cycles. Drug use spawns itself. At the start of addiction, drugs are used because they are pleasurable, the drinker likes the high, or the prescription user likes the relief. Those are the motives for continuing. Later, drinking or drugging causes silly or outrageous behavior. Shame and guilt then join the addict's growing list of reasons for drinking. At some point, that list includes drinking to solve problems. And finally, addiction creates anxiety, resentment, bitterness and isolation, and those emotions become additional reasons for drinking. Withdrawal is simply one more reason for continuing, and it reaches its peak when one drinks for little more than a reprieve from the terror that stopping drinking has created.

Eventually, addiction needs no push from an outside force to keep it going. Family members blame themselves for an addict's continued drinking, not realizing that their loved one will continue his use with or without them. Addiction survives divorce and separation. Eventually addiction generates all the force it needs to continue. It becomes autonomous, self-sustaining. It has a life of its own.

Drives and Cravings: Addicts know well what science has a difficult time proving even exists, craving. Drug cravings occur during withdrawal. They are not to be equated with withdrawal since cravings exist before one becomes physically dependent, and they continue long after he has withdrawn. Cravings are not provoked only by emotional distress. Pleasurable associations trigger them too. Sometimes cravings come without any apparent stimulus. To attribute cravings exclusively to psychological pain is misleading. To ascribe them to pleasurable stimuli alone is equally misleading. Furthermore, because cravings are different with different drugs, it seems more reasonable to attribute them to physical processes than to psychological ones. Cigarette smokers describe craving for nicotine as quick pulse-like urges which come in prolonged and repeated waves. Alcoholics, sober for six months, describe alcohol craving as sudden and viselike, lasting sometimes minutes or sometimes hours.

A reason craving is difficult to pinpoint is that careless use of language clouds the issue. The words, craving, drive and urge, have been used interchangeably making it impossible to determine whether they describe one or several different phenomena. Addicts know cravings regardless of how confusing language has come to be.

Metaphors for Craving: Non-addicts find it difficult to understand the force that drives addiction. That force is better understood through metaphors. It is a desire for a world alcohol fashions. An ideal world where life is serene, where snow is pure, and where birds never cackle. It is longing for a world where imperfection does not exist - the men are strong, the women good looking, and the children above average. Addicts respond in Pavlovian ways to certain events and certain arrangements of people and places. A fragrance, a particular restaurant, and a well scrubbed home, even putting on a tuxedo, might trigger an urge to drink. For addicts, time distorts in a way similar to the way it distorts for a child at Christmas. Sober time seems as long as Christmas Eve, which is an eternity from the child's point of view. Drinking time is like Christmas Day, which is over in a blink. The addictive urge is the unreachable itch in the middle of your back. It is magnetic, drawn to drinkers and drinking, druggers and drugging. A new addiction is a love affair, complete with the wonder and enchantment of it all. An old addiction is a burnt out marriage or the debt on the car that is being towed away. No matter how painful past drug use has been, addicts believe that the next time the drug will deliver the power, joy, magic, clarity, excitement, and romance it used to.

If cravings paid attention to logic or fear, if cravings heeded negative reinforcement, then addicts who have lost jobs, families, self respect, and lungs because of nicotine and alcohol would not crave those drugs. But addiction is deaf to logic. It flies in the face of common sense.

As addiction progresses, it goes from pleasant diversion to center stage. It displaces families, friends, hobbies, jobs, recreations, goals and self-respect. Though he denies it, the drug is an addict's preoccupation. He cherishes drugs. He loves them.

What any individual values may be judged by where he spends his resources: his time, his money, and his mind. When drinking structures a chunk of one's time, spends most of his available money, chooses his friends, replaces other recreations, consumes his psychic energy, and plots his lifestyle - when he risks his life for drugs, then the force which drives him is as powerful as any force we know - as powerful as the will to survive. When an alcoholic ends a marriage rather than stop drinking, it is drinking he loves. And addiction is a cruel lover.

10

COMPLICATED ADDICTIONS

Because addicts are human beings, some will suffer from a psychiatric disorder, not because of that disorder but along with it. Others may find that complications, health problems and repeated failures at treatment call for special care if they are to recover, if they are to be able to function.

Co-Occurring Disorders: The numbers of patients with bipolar disorder (manic depression) who also suffer with addiction is significant and exceeds 60%, according to some researchers (Regier, Farmer, Rae, Locke, Keith, Judd, & Goodwin, 1990). Thus, bipolar patients are well advised to maintain a high level of suspicion about their alcohol and recreational drug use. What is less clear, are the numbers of alcoholics who suffer from a psychiatric illness. Those estimates vary widely, in part because those estimates are complicated by a couple of problems. When they are drunk, alcoholics and other addicts create all sorts of psychiatric smoke which look like symptoms of a co-occurring disorder. And if addicts who are in the throes of early recovery are not weeded out of a studied group, they will mislead researchers into inflated numbers simply because they are in the throes of early recovery and they appear psychiatric.

Early recovery is a difficult time fraught with problems and issues. It can last quite a long time – six months to a year for some and for a few even longer. Many an alcoholic is depressed and anxious, sleepless for several months, fearful now and again, irritable, sad, agitated, anxious, depressed, and resentful during it. Veteran A. A. members recall early recovery as a time when the ego vacillates between a "Great Big I" and a "Poor Little Me" even within a day or a week or a month. Confusion about identity is commonplace for anyone who has based his identity on intoxicated experiences. And for those whose drug problem started in their teens, addiction not only delays, but also complicates, normal maturation. Hopelessness is a part of the picture too. Early recovery is a strange, new world. As one recovering alcoholic put it, "You wake up and wonder, 'Where will I go, who will I go with, and what will I do once I get there?'" It is an unpleasant time for all, and nearly unbearable for those who remain untreated and unsupported during it.

Untreated abstinent addicts are not a happy lot. They overcompensate for the loss of a drug by plunging into other compulsive behaviors: work, sex, gambling, and eating among them. They resent having a chronic disease. They are separated from their buddies. They carry guilt about the past, shame about the present and uncertainty about the future. They look "psychiatric." It is little wonder that recovering alcoholics have been diagnosed with disorders which after a year of A. A. meetings and Twelve Step work are undetectable. Trying to tease out which patient has an independent and coexisting psychiatric diagnosis, and which suffers from early recovery itself, is difficult in all cases, and impossible in some without letting time pass.

Psychotic and Mood Disorders

Certain psychiatric disorders are easier to detect than others. Even a layman has little difficulty recognizing schizophrenia when it is out of control, even if he does not know what to call it. Full blown mania is relatively easily recognized too. But depression and hypomanic (not full blown mania) behavior, panic and anxiety disorders can fool nearly everyone, except those with an experienced and trained eye schooled in addiction and early recovery. Sometimes, even they have to let time pass before the truth emerges.

With mild to moderate depression, a treatment professional may be able to afford to wait, and an alcoholic might be able to endure the wait, before deciding that he needs to be treated for an independent depression along with addiction. The same professional has considerably less time to allow psychosis, mania or severe depression to go untreated. And the patient who has gotten through detoxification, but who is still hallucinating, has to be considered as suffering with an independent psychiatric disorder and treated as such.

Character Disorders

Character Disorders are especially difficult to distinguish from addictive behavior. The impact of drinking and drugging on personality is substantial. After all, merely acquiring an illegal drug requires the user to break the law. Is that a socio-cultural phenomenon or symptomatic of an anti-social personality? Addicts abuse spouses. Is that personality or out of control drunkenness? People who are drunk violate all sorts of boundaries; have intoxicated experiences which confuse them about their identity; experience extreme emotional outbursts; and find intimacy without drugs difficult. They need help and they want help. But they push it away, especially if sobriety is the form help takes. Is that borderline behavior or the product of addiction? Addicts lose jobs and the motivation to find them. At age 35 they end up out of work and living with their parents. Is that dependency or marijuana? Every day addicts cycle through guilt, arrogance, and resentment. Is that emerging personality or the ordinary rhythms of recovery? Shame, all by itself, warps human personality and produces intense feelings and avoidant and compensatory behavior. Women alcoholics who are stuck with the cultural stereotype for what is considered appropriate feminine behavior are going to be overwhelmed by the shame of having an addiction and avoid treating it because of that shame.

Statistics of co-occurring disorders in the addicted population are useful only when researchers limit their data to those whose history satisfies criteria in the *Diagnostic and Statistical* Manual *of Mental Disorder* (APA, 1994) pre-morbidly (before addiction) or during a period of "treated" abstinence. Knowing such data will help treatment workers have a clearer idea of how common certain psychiatric disorders are and will aid in exploring how to detect them early in the recovery process.

Detecting a Second Disorder Early: In the late 1970s, some psychiatrists (not all) did not accept alcoholism as a legitimate illness, even though the criterion for its diagnosis was included in the Diagnostic Manual. Many an alcoholic slipped under the radar either because the radar wasn't looking for him, or when the radar picked up intoxication, it was interpreted as a blip indicating a psychological problem. By the early 1990s, addiction counselors (again, not all of them) told patients that if they treated their addiction, their psychiatric symptoms would go away, which, in fact, did happen for some. But for a number of others, signs of an existing or impending psychological problem were misinterpreted, minimized or ignored, thus making early recovery even more painful than it had to be.

Today, a middle ground is emerging as main-stream. Some alcoholics and other drug addicts do suffer from a co-occurring disorder, though most do not. Along with that notion is that treating the two disorders simultaneously is the preferred approach, provided that treating both simultaneously is even possible. That approach, however, forces us to answer all too obvious and hard questions. Are there specific signs even early in recovery that indicate the presence of a psychiatric disorder? And when another diagnosis is detected, how should it be treated – with drugs, psychotherapy or both?

Bipolar Disorder Foreshadowed

Patients on cocaine, methamphetamine, and crack (generally, the stimulant drugs), experience racing thoughts and consecutive sleepless days and nights simply because of their drug use. They appear manic, but is that a co-occurring bipolar disorder breaking through or is that the drug? Persistent pursuit and near-exclusive use of stimulants may presage a diagnosis of bipolar disorder. However, determining what is a matter of drug of choice and what might foreshadow bipolar disorder can be troublesome. This is especially true when the patient is a teenager or in his early twenties who is both at just the right age for early signs of bipolar disorder, but who is also at just the right age for going for the gusto and trying anything that will vivify life. Racing thoughts and sleepless days on end suggest bipolar mania if those behaviors appear during a period of treated abstinence; persist well after the half life of the drug has run its course; or if those symptoms were present pre-morbidly (before addiction). The patient who is manic and hypomanic after six to eight weeks of sustained abstinence; spends money in a binge way; stays awake for days on end; and has racing thoughts, should be directed to an addiction trained psychiatrist to begin considering when to start and how to treat a bipolar disorder. This is especially true if the patient has been working an addiction recovery program and has support for it.

Addicted patients whose history has included mixed states, depression and mania at the same time, ought to maintain a high level of suspicion that a second psychiatric disorder is at work in them. This is very likely if the depression is deep, the mania frenetic, and the mixed state has had a long history.

Signs of a Co-Existing Depression in Early Recovery

Active alcoholism mimics depression. The prospect of a life of abstinence is depressing. Early recovery is depressing. The appearance of depression in early recovery is quite frankly the expected state. It should be diagnosed as independent and co-occurring only when an addicted person has been clean and sober for four or more months, has an A. A. sponsor and is attending A. A. meetings regularly. But depression, even early in recovery, should be suspected if the addicted person finds he cannot sleep or sleeps too much; finds increasingly that he awakens early; has a poor appetite; broods about the past; has intrusive morbid or suicidal thoughts; finds it hard to get out of bed, go to work, enjoy a game of cards; is irritable over little things; and/or finds putting together sentences without laboring for a thought difficult. Those symptoms in a treated, recovering addict should lead one to seek a psychiatrist trained to treat a co-existing depressive disorder.

Detecting an Anxiety Disorder Early in Recovery

Anxiety disorders are more difficult to tease out because anxiety is a common early abstinence problem. It is even more difficult to treat since the kinds of medications that tamp down anxiety are cross tolerant and cross addictive with alcohol. If one's anxiety has appeared only after years of heavy drinking and drugging, who can say whether it is independent of, or leftover from, long-term addiction? It might just go away. And yet, an A. A. member, who has been clean and sober for several months, might experience a cluster (not necessarily all) of the following symptoms: he wakes up anxious regularly for weeks on end; dreads going to sleep; shakes when he goes outside; feels trapped in elevators; has a knot in his stomach when going to work; hyperventilates in public; and whose palms sweat, voice quakes, and knees wobble if asked to speak in public (to an extent everybody experiences some of those problems when on display). All of these are clear enough warnings that he should seek a psychiatrist who understands cross addiction and is willing to walk the tightrope when it comes to deciding whether to prescribe, what to prescribe, for how long, under what circumstances, how to supervise and when to discontinue it.

Treating Dual Disorders: Which Comes First?   Dr. Scott Aaronson of The Retreat Program at Sheppard Pratt in Baltimore, Maryland puts it simply and elegantly. "When your car is at the bottom of a lake, you don't send a scuba diver down to fix it. You get it off the bottom." He is also skilled in intuiting which treatment, psychiatric or addiction, will get the vehicle above water and dry.

In the majority of cases, psychiatric treatment is wasted on drinking alcoholics and drug using addicts. Recreational drug use reduces or cancels the effect of anti-depressant medication. Simultaneous use of anti-depressants, benzodiazepines and alcohol clouds the psychiatric picture and is dangerous as well. Drunken patients are not motivated to pursue treatment for anything, much less two things. And alcoholics whose drinking is out of control keep adding crises, stressors, problems, and other unignorable issues to the psychic mill. All these need fixing, or band-aiding at least, and so productive therapy is delayed and further complicated. For the majority, sobriety is the priority, either the first order of business or simultaneous with a psychiatric treatment, if one is certain that a psychiatric disorder is indeed present and a patient is motivated to recover from addiction. There are exceptions, of course.

Early Recovery and the Actively Addicted Schizophrenic Patient

An actively addicted schizophrenic patient is unable to process learning about addiction in any meaningful way. Each of his two illnesses magnifies the other, rendering him incapable of understanding what is at the root of his troubles. These patients are not ready to consider whether their alcohol and marijuana use creates additional problems or not. They are at times even unable to know when their behavior is out of control, much less why it is. The nature of addictive disease and the subtlety of its denial require too fine a set of distinctions for someone who is psychotic. Reason itself is askew as the understandable product of the two illnesses. Getting them out of psychosis comes first. Integration is the first order of business, and treatment professionals who work with schizophrenics at this time need the patience to deal with their drinking and pot smoking. They also need the determination to continue encouraging abstinence, accepting all the while that abstinence might not happen right away.

Treating Mania in Early Recovery

Bipolar patients whose mania is out of control or those with psychotic features feel far too powerful to see how denial works in them much less deal with it. Coming back to earth is a necessary first step until they are settled enough to learn about addiction and begin considering whether they have lost control.

Treating Other Psychiatric Disorders in Early Recovery

But what about anti-social patients, the ones who used to be called sociopaths? Can we afford to wait for them to burn out before pushing treatment for addiction at the same time as we start working on their other problems? What about the patient who is both drunk and depressed, but not suicidal and not psychotic? Can't he be expected to cope with accepting an addiction and a depression diagnosis, while at the same time stopping his alcohol and recreational drug use, and then start anti-depressant medication? How about the anxious patient who is nevertheless able to function, go to work, and participate in family functions? Can't he benefit from a two-pronged treatment? What about patients who are self medicating with both recreational drugs and psychiatric medications? Can't those patients be persuaded to see that self medication and addiction are not mutually exclusive, and that dual treatment is possible and effective?

Guidelines for Simultaneous Treatment: In the past, treatment for the doubly troubled patient involved a sequential approach, treating one or the other disorder first. Usually it was addiction that came first. Today the treatment world prefers treating both disorders simultaneously. Simultaneous treatment, however, must avoid some common and precarious traps, which are listed below:

- Dealing with psychic material from the past, if it greatly increases a patient's level of stress, may be asking too much of an addict who is already dealing with early recovery. He has stress enough as it is. It is true that effective therapy does involve some level of stress, but knowing how much stress is productive, and at what point it becomes counter-productive, requires a compassionate therapist willing to walk that fine line.

- Medicating post-acute withdrawal and the ordinary turmoil of early recovery simply enables addicts to continue to use addictive drugs with what appears the sanction of the medical community. A patient so treated thinks his addiction minor. The key here is knowing what garden variety early recovery looks like, what is extraordinary, what sorts of behaviors point to an underlying illness and which are part of getting over addiction. Early recovery is a topic that has been little researched, and yet knowing the line between it and underlying illness is crucial to the psychiatrist who hopes to individualize treatment. "No pain, no gain" is trite because it is true. Too much pain, however, is never useful.

- Counseling that loses its balance – the balance necessary to treat two disorders not only simultaneously but equally - is counter-productive.   The therapist, who focuses more on one disorder than the other, persuades his patient to do the same.

- Simultaneous treatment that includes careful education about which medications are useful and under what circumstances, and which are not, is essential. For the psychiatrically complicated alcoholic, the view that all drugs are okay is as harmful as the notion that all drugs are evil.

- Treatment for the dually diagnosed patient ought to include warnings such as: the possible return of denial; the temptation to abandon treatment for one or the other disorder; the fact that members of the recovering community will not always understand and be compassionate to those with two problems; and that out of ignorance, some well-meaning people will encourage stopping necessary medication

- Communicating clearly to patients that their doubly troubled condition involves a peculiar irony. The two conditions are both connected and not connected. Treating one disorder will not cause the other to go away. Yet not treating one will cause the other disorder to get worse, with each disorder in turn making the other worse in a continuing cycle.

Anyone who works with the dually-diagnosed population in their first and second efforts at abstinence ought to be aware that early treatments may be seed-planting operations. Only later will an alcoholic get sober and thank those who were patient with him at the start.

Denial in the Psychiatrically-Complicated Addict: Treatment profession-als who work with psychiatrically complicated cases, especially pre-scription addicts, can bet they will deal with the patient's common rationalization that his drug use is all about, and only about, self-medication, and that he uses mood altering drugs simply and singly to deal with pain. There is a piece of truth there, but only half of the truth. Dismissing it out of hand and confronting a self-medicating addict that his use is not of the self-medicating variety is counter-productive. They do self medicate. What these patients convenient-ly forget is that in addition to their self-medicating, there is another force at work in them – addiction.

Prescription addicts forget that they use drugs when they are stressed, and they use them when they are not stressed. Sometimes they take them just in case. They smoke pot and drink alcohol – sometimes to relieve sadness, but also to enhance happiness, to calm down, to reward themselves for an achievement, to enjoy a good movie, to relax after work, to take pleasure in the euphoria, and to avoid dealing with the ambiguity of mixed states. They overlook that theirs is an unhealthy and unfortunately high tolerance for mood altering drugs, which is a problem in and of itself whether one is self-medicating or partying. Even when self medication is the mo-tive for taking a first dose, they fail to take into account that they take a second, third and fourth. They lose control and end up drunk or drugged and wasted. If all a sufferer wants is relief from psychic pain, he doesn't have to take double and triple doses to achieve it. And surely, cocaine is not the drug of choice for an agitated person in emotional pain, much less when the drug is "crack." When insisting that his objective is pain relief, the self medicating addict overlooks his love of his drug. Most prescription addicts cannot identify with "getting high" as what they aim for. "Getting into the zone" better expresses in words what they look for and love about their drug. And they do love "the zone." Love is not self-medication.

Drug Use and the Non-Addicted Psychiatric Patient: It would be short-sighted not to mention that there are psychiatric patients who drink and smoke marijuana along with their prescription drugs, both to deal with pain and as recreation. Some of them do not lose control. They have not developed alarming drug tolerance, and they have not persisted in using such drugs beyond reason. Obvious as it may be, this is to say no more than that there are psychiatric patients who are not addicted to psychoactive drugs but who do use them. Some patients have two diagnoses, while other have one.

Even the psychiatric patient who is not addicted, however, is best advised to avoid recreational drug use if he hopes to gain from pharmacotherapy and psychotherapy. The recreational drug-using patient defeats his psychiatric medication if he is on one. Anti-depressants have a difficult time doing their job when they have to contend with the depressant alcohol. Besides, it makes more sense to take a clear head to therapy rather than a drugged or drug-affected one. The self-medicating patient leaks, forgets, deflates, reduces, and diminishes the material he brings to a therapy session. Important psychic material finds expression under conditions and in situations that do not allow for dealing with it effectively. It is what some have called "therapy leak." To dull psychic pain by using drugs in addition to those prescribed for it, weakens motivation for psychotherapy. It takes the pressure off.

Accepting Two Diagnoses: If you think it is difficult to accept that you are depressed, consider the challenge when addiction is added to the list of problems you need to accept. For one patient, the impact of learning he carried an alcoholism diagnosis was so disconcerting that for twenty-four hours he was so acutely suicidal that he asked for staff help in dealing with the news. He had not been suicidal when he walked into treatment. He came in an exhausted, mildly depressed patient confused about his identity, and suffering from post traumatic stress. He knew he had been drinking too much, but because he was still functioning, he did not think of himself as an alcoholic. In his words, "the diagnosis (of addiction) devastated me." And only a chance call from his wife promising her unquestioned and absolute support helped him through the next couple of days. In truth, this patient had been thinking about how excessive his drinking had become and was wondering if there were times it was out of control. At some level of consciousness, he had already done some self diagnostic work. Most often denial erodes. Once in a great while it collapses. In his case it collapsed.

Treating depression all by itself involves learning, adaptation and change. It involves psychotherapy and sometimes a medication that works. It involves a rearrangement of one's mental furniture. Add addiction treatment and the depressed patient faces treating depression without the relief that tranquilizers and recreational alcohol and drugs offer. He adds to his agenda another long laundry list of things to do at a time when he has little energy to get out of bed, much less take on new and unfamiliar activities. Go to self help meetings - ninety meetings in ninety days at the start. Get a sponsor and phone contacts, learn the language of recovery, begin working the A. A. program, admit you are powerless, and struggle with the concept of a Higher Power. Beware of slippery places and slippery people. Dismantle your denial system. Get alcohol and other drugs out of the house. Decide who must know about your condition and why. Develop a liking for group interaction, deflate your ego, and learn to ask for help. Sever contact with those who supply you with drugs, meet a whole new group of people, and accept that your family will be angry and mistrustful for a while. Consider an intensive outpatient program with five or six treatment contacts each week, attend A. A. meetings six out of seven days a week, and on the seventh day go to another A. A. meeting. At the very least, go to group therapy so you can grieve and deal with the strain of socializing with friends who still drink, and change the way you celebrate New Years, St. Paddy's Day, Memorial Day, Fourth of July, Labor Day, and Christmas. Finally, don't take a sleeping pill even if you can't sleep and don't take a tranquilizer even if a loved one dies. Also, consider going to a halfway house for sixty days to help get a good start on maintaining sobriety. And have a Merry Christmas! Ain't recovery swell?

Recovering Alcoholics and   Nothing provides more convincing
Mood Altering Prescriptions: evidence of the danger of prescribing
psychoactive medication to an alcoholic than witnessing the devasta-
tion when both prescription use and recreational use are out of control. Such a patient is "under the influence" twenty-four, seven. Life
is processed, drugged and drug-affected. Anyone who has worked
through protracted post acute withdrawal with an addict who has
been hooked on benzodiazepines knows the patient would have been
better off if he could have avoided the use of benzodiazepines rather
than have to deal with the stresses that come with withdrawing from
them. Anxiety, emotional augmentation, hypersensitivity, and panic
are problems the recovering person wakes up with.

A psychiatrist should get a license to prescribe drugs for addicted
patients only after he or she has demonstrated compassion and has
proven willingness to torture with the decision when he pulls out a
prescription pad in the presence of an alcoholic. Given those cautions, are there ever times when an addict may need to take a mood
altering drug? There are.

There was a time that recovering veterans encouraged newcomers to stop anti-depressant medication, cautioned schizophrenics to
be wary of taking anti-psychotic drugs, and told bipolar addicts that
they were not yet abstinent and recovering until they stopped their
Lithium. Ignorance, not sadism, was behind the recommendation.
Veterans in recovery were poignantly aware of cases in which their
recovering friends had been prescribed drugs that were harmful.
Some of them simply did not know the nature and action of anti-
depressants, anti-psychotics and mood stabilizers. Thankfully, that
problem is fading into the past. A good many A. A. members who
initially resisted taking needed drugs of that type learned that such
drugs aid in their recovery, not interfere with it. Often they learned it
the hard way. Anti-depressants and mood stabilizers are not dependence-causing drugs. Today, the question has become whether in
addition to anti-depressants and mood stabilizers, an addict should
be prescribed a drug which *is* dependence-causing and potentially
addictive.

There are conditions for which an addict may need to take a drug to which he is vulnerable. Exclude hypnotherapists, and only purists, sadists, and masochists insist on surgery without anesthetics before and pain killers after. The rest of the world recognizes such use as both necessary and risky, and therefore, needing to be short-term and supervised. Dental surgery and the pain that follows may require that those with a low threshold for pain be sedated during surgery and prescribed pain killers after, or else they will lose their teeth rather than make an appointment to see a dentist. Finally and obviously, a carefully monitored prescription for a drug that will sedate an acutely suicidal patient is life-saving. Dead patients cease to be patients.

The safest approach for a recovering A. A. member in the above situations is to let his A. A. sponsor know that he is scheduled for surgery, is about to have a root canal or a wisdom tooth extracted, or is under the care of a psychiatrist because he has been thinking that he would be better off dead. Then you hope the A. A. sponsor understands, and if he doesn't, find a new one.

Mood Altering Drugs in the Troublesome Cases

The dilemma for treatment professionals comes when severely impaired addicts, for any of a variety of reasons, have failed again and again and again and again to get sober, with each relapse moving closer and closer to life threatening symptoms. The dilemma comes when drug maintenance programs are under discussion – methadone maintenance and buprenorphine treatment. The tough case is that of a depressed patient who is not suicidal but suffers from severe agitation, whose anti-depressant has not yet begun to work, and is unable to sleep or eat, even after several months of treated abstinence. The problem comes when a recovering alcoholic is rendered immobile by anxiety over a period of time and can't leave the house because of panic. The dilemma comes when an addict suffers from a seizure disorder, migraines, a brain injury, or trauma.

What is desirable is not always what is possible. Total abstinence may be the first choice for addicts. But when the choice is between mood altering drugs or suicide, drug use unarguably outweighs abstinence as a necessary treatment, not merely the treatment of choice. It is the best example in which "harm reduction" becomes the objective. Abstinence can come later. Harm reduction is first.

A patient with a seizure disorder may be in harm's way because of seizures. He may need to take a potentially addictive anti-seizure medication when no other solution is available. His use of the prescribed drug will need monitoring, not just prescribing. Brain injured addicts may need medication too, and not just a script but close supervision of its use if an adjunctive drug is to be part of the solution and not more of the problem. Chronic pain patients need carefully managed pain-relieving drugs, if they have exhausted non-drug alternatives to pain management. There are such alternatives. Hypnosis, acupuncture, chiropractic treatment, physical therapy, meditation, and yoga have helped recovering alcoholics in chronic pain. Addicts are best advised to approach solutions for other problems conservatively. First try a no risk alternative, then an option with minimal risk, before you go on to solutions which involve serious risk and the potential for prolonged relapse. After all, untreated pain puts a recovering addict at risk for relapse as well.

Given that any alcoholic or other addict must be aware of his own drug-seeking behavior, there are cases in which post acute withdrawal is so intense (emphasis on *so intense*) that the likelihood that one will survive it without relapsing argues for a carefully supervised, ideally short term prescription as preferable to a prolonged and destructive relapse. But for how long? And which drug? How to monitor it? Having a prescription is not enough. Its use has to be watched.

Certainly putting a recovering alcoholic on a tranquilizer is contraindicated if his response is that he "loves" the tranquilizer. That's just switching drug of choice. When the pleasure response exceeds pain relief, both patient and doctor should know that the drug is the wrong one. Both must then cooperate in the search for a drug that relieves distress without producing a delightful euphoric "high." Even then the prescriber must be committed to managing the prescription with care. Both addict and prescriber should struggle weekly about when to discontinue such use. Even when the prescribed drug is not the addict's drug of choice, and even if the addict finds the drug not particularly pleasurable, he will still suffer withdrawal when he tries to stop it - with post acute withdrawal to follow for some time after that. When a benzodiazepine has become the *necessary stop-gap* solution for a critical problem, both prescriber and drug taker need to know that they have started a process which will have consequences well into the future.

One reason for the continuing struggle between psychiatrists and addiction counselors is that the psychiatrist who prescribes a benzo-diazepine is often not privy to the patient's suffering from protracted withdrawal from that benzodiazepine a year later. And the A. A. sponsor who helps his friend get through protracted benzodiazepine withdrawal has not witnessed first hand the severe agitation which compelled the psychiatrist to prescribe it in the first place the year before. Both psychiatrists and addiction specialists need to share their experiences on the ends of that anxiety spectrum if treatment is going to be careful and useful for individuals.

Maintenance and Drug Substitute Treatments: Experience has taught the treat-ment community that addiction does not come in one form with a single potency, but at varying levels of intensity and severity. The ad-dictive pull is quite simply stronger in some than in others. Although there are a range of reasons why abstinent recovery is particularly difficult in certain cases, the fact is that there are addicts who chroni-cally relapse. There are others who put together a sober year but fall back into sixteen years drunk, drugged, and disabled, and there are those who find that cravings are intense and persistent. There are addicts whose brains have learned to work better with drugs than without them, some whose depression is prolonged and deep, and some whose addiction is complicated by a chronic health problem, a seizure disorder, or brain damage. To hold that all of them relapse because they lack character, courage and will does not explain the total community of chronic relapsers.

In the case of an addiction that has had a devastating impact on its victim over a long time (with severe, even life-threatening symp-

toms), when attempts at abstinence have failed repeatedly, harm reduction and maintenance care may be necessary (at least for a period
of time) rather than expecting total abstinence from the outset. Such
treatment starts with a prescription. It then moves to regular follow
up to monitor the patient's compliance so that the process moves in
the direction of the personal changes that will end with healthy, and
hopefully abstinent, recovery.

Sad as it may be, there are addicts who may need maintenance
for a long time, and some who may *need* it for a lifetime. For these
patients A. A. is not a comfortable program, and attending meetings
is not a comfortable experience.

The risk of advertising a drug maintenance program to large
numbers of recovering addicts on their first-ever sober week is that
many will volunteer to be included in the group that continues psychoactive drugs. They may or may not belong. Time will tell.

Methadone Maintenance

Methadone maintenance is based on the concept that narcotic
addicts have a better chance of achieving abstinent recovery if they
move gradually in that direction. The aim is to take an addict off
one narcotic, such as heroin, and "addict" him to another, Methadone. This is done with the hope of creating a period of re-education
and rehabilitation without the patient's needing to seek and use short
acting narcotic drugs multiple times a day and being "out of it" between doses. At one time in its history "maintenance" treatment was
intended to be "temporary maintenance" that would move toward
abstinent recovery. That goal has not always been realized, and there
are addicts who have been maintained on methadone year after year
after year, even as many as twenty years and more.

Methadone treatment may be regarded a success if and when it
reduces harm and helps an addict reintegrate into a socially useful
role. When it leads to detoxification from methadone itself, Methadone Treatment may be considered phenomenally successful. On
the other hand, a methadone-maintained addict who takes his methadone but also continues to use other drugs, who breaks the law, is

on the nod, and costs society money to house, feed and incarcerate him - that could hardly be regarded a success. In such cases, methadone is as enabling as any other kind of enabling, the equivalent of Supplemental Drug Treatment. Treatment professionals might want to deal with those who abuse a "maintenance program" by throwing them out of treatment. That's not as easy emotionally as first it seems.

Buprenorphine Treatment

Buprenorphine is a relatively new drug. It is touted to have promise in reducing the harm that narcotics addicts suffer from their illegal and dangerous behavior, and the unpredictable potency and purity of the drugs they use. Buprenorphine might replace Methadone maintenance, as it has in Europe, with fewer problems than Methadone. It produces minimal euphoria with the advantage that a patient can obtain it in a doctor's office. This provides a more discreet way which is one that avoids the possibility that a motivated patient may meet some elements that will prey on them at a clinic.

Some people are addicted; some are physically dependent; and some are both. Addiction and physical dependence are not identical. Suboxone, the trade name for one form of Buprenorphine has helped chronic pain patients whose past pain management resulted in their becoming physically dependent on a narcotic. Suboxone may help the patient with chronic pain and those with health and/or emotional problems whose dependence on a drug has rendered them dysfunctional and who are motivated to come off the drug. The patient who has been physically dependent, but in no other way acts like a drug addict, may find the switch to Suboxone helpful. The hope is that Suboxone will return dysfunctional patients to productive lives without their being dysfunctionally high and without necessitating the criminal activity associated with "scoring narcotics."

Buprenorphine treatment, however, is not a cure all or a miracle. Not everyone is an appropriate candidate for its use. And there are risks. Narcotic addicts must stop using their favorite narcotic for a day or more before initiating Buprenorphine treatment to avoid dangerous drug interactions. Buprenorphine maintenance will help those who are motivated to reeducate and recover, but it will be no more successful than its predecessor if those receiving it continue to use other drugs. Buprenorphine is a narcotic drug, and so dependence on it does develop. Eventually a user who stops taking it will withdraw from it. Pain patients can be helped, but not all pain patients are willing to let go of the side benefit of a mood altering drug. Even when its primary purpose is pain relief, there are some who want to hold on to the euphoria. They are not the best candidates for Buprenorphine treatment.

To jump to substitute one drug for another after a single relapse in one's first effort at treatment is careless and sloppy. Drug substitution treatment is likely to prove helpful only when care in exercised in the patient selection process. That is, defining for whom substitution is the most appropriate treatment.

"Who is best served?" "Who is an appropriate candidate for our program?" These are questions any facility must answer unless it proposes to be all things to all people. "For whom is Buprenorphine the right treatment?" is as important as determining what is an optimal dose.

If Hippocrates had not said, "First, no harm," doctors would have an easier time consigning what appear to be hopeless cases to fend for themselves.

Pills for Recovery? Disulfram, the generic name for Antabuse (a drug that will make an alcoholic very sick if he drinks while taking it), has been around, and has been a useful adjunct to treatment for a time. It is helpful for a very specific target population, namely motivated alcoholics who want to avoid impulsive drinking. If they drink before they think they get sick. And even though Antabuse does not stop an alcoholic from taking a first drink (some do drink on Antabuse), it will keep him from taking the second one. And so, even if Antabuse doesn't preclude a slip, it may prevent a slide.

In addition to helping a patient avoid impulsive drinking, Antabuse can provide a measure of protection for the alcoholic who remains conflicted about whether he has the disease. Antabuse may provide him an abstinent break while he works through answering, internalizing and accepting his diagnosis. Antabuse is also a significant aid for those who live or work in environments where temptation and availability are everywhere; it has helped bartenders recover. Quite simply, Antabuse is most effective when it frees the mind by eliminating the all-day-long-debate over whether to drink today. The decision is made once in the morning when the pill is swallowed.

Antabuse is obtained by prescription, and candidates for it must be medically cleared before starting the drug since drinking on it can cause serious consequences for those with a cardio-vascular problem. A patient with a heart problem who has a history of impulsive drinking is not a good Antabuse patient. Otherwise side effects are minimal, and the drug is rather safe for those cleared for its use.

Antabuse will not help an unmotivated patient; it will not help those who plan to drink. Antabuse does not create motivation. Abstinence may help to reinforce the motivation to continue with abstinence, and to that extent Antabuse may help in the long run. However, an alcoholic who has no motivation for treatment at all is not a good Antabuse candidate. Someone has to want to get sober, and further want to remain abstinent at least for a while. Then Antabuse will help if cravings hit.

It is a mistake to think that Antabuse is treatment. It is an adjunct, not treatment itself. A simple pill does not solve a complex disease, and so the best time to take Antabuse may well be on the way to an A. A. meeting.

There are narcotic addicts who have been helped by Naltrexone, a drug that diminishes the intensity of the euphoric feeling if a narcotic is used. The hope is that after a while, a narcotic user will tire of diminished intoxication, pursuing "the high" and the processes of getting, cooking, injecting and maintaining the works when the end result is not worth the effort. How long it might take an addict to burn out of his love of intoxication is an issue that Naltrexone does not address. Naltrexone hopes for burn out. It does not cause it.

The search for helpful addiction recovery drugs will continue be-cause for manufacturers there is money in the pursuit. Finding a pill that will quick-fix an addiction is appealing to therapists who battle every day trying to help addicts recover. It's less work. Addicts themselves are eager for a miracle pill, one that promises to be less painful than "white-knuckling" it; a pill would be an easier softer way. Families are attracted to any quick cure that will lessen their fear. All these groups long for a treatment that is quick, painless, and predictable. Nicotine substitutes prove that.

A pill that eliminates craving is going to be helpful to an extent. If science can invent a drug that speeds up brain healing, that too will be worth spending national dollars to pursue. But drugs that reduce craving and enhance brain healing pre-suppose that an addict will want to recover in the first place. Lucky is the entrepreneur who develops a motivation pill. He or she will be a billionaire overnight since the demand will be massive. Its potential customers would range beyond the addicted population to those who need such a pill but who are ironically not motivated enough to take it in the first place. Drugs do not create motivation for recovery; they help after motivation is in place. Will there ever be a pill that helps an addict tire of intoxication? Will a drug be found that erodes denial? Science has not even begun to consider whether a "Hope Drug," one that will bring hope to the hopeless, is in the future. Research has just begun to wonder about what configuration of chemicals will diminish the love that is the driving force of addiction. Is there a pill that will en-able enablers to stop enabling? Finding medications for any of these purposes is going to require good science, imagination, knowledge of addiction, and hard work.

Denial, love, hopelessness, and enabling are the powers behind addiction. Treatment will remain as much an art as a science as long as those forces drive it.

11

TEEN DRINKING AND DRUG USE

Why?   Why do kids drink? Why do kids drunk? Why do kids do drugs? These are quite different questions, each with its own answer depending on the age and sex of the teen.

As the force which drives teen alcohol, marijuana and other drug use, "peer pressure" is a myth. Peer acceptance describes more accurately why even middle school youngsters pick up their first drink or drug ever, and why they continue. It is not a matter of one kid pushing another to drink. It is about the other's desire to fit in, to be part of the crowd, to be included, and to be cool in the eyes of his peers. It is, in short, about belonging. If it seems driven, it is driven by the dread of being left out, avoided, isolated, lonely, and "out of it." The "pressure" is inside the kid. There is no more important agenda for an eleven year old than to have friends. That is why he takes a swig of that first drink, toke of that first joint or a dose of that first drug – to be part of his group, to belong. The force is within.

As one nears the end of high school, peer acceptance has even less to do with why older teens drink. And peer pressure has nothing to do with it by then. Why the sixteen and seventeen year old junior and senior members of the lacrosse, volley ball, debating teams or dramatic society drink at a party has changed. By that time, a youngster has found his peer group; he is accepted somewhere in the peer system.

181

Peer pressure has even less to do with why older teens get drunk. Pressure has absolutely nothing to do with why a group of them get together to put on a "kegger" in the woods or at some unsuspecting parents' home. By the end of high school, out of control alcohol and drug use has become one of the ways kids celebrate. It's about bonding with classmates. It's a way "to let her rip" and to act out sexually, without guilt and responsibility. Perhaps, in a less than conscious way, it's a way of creating memories for the future. It's a way to have stories to tell in adulthood about the wild, crazy, and hair-raising adventures they had when they were young. It is their way of saying, "We were here, we were young, and we were alive!"

Even adults, when encouraged to give other than knee jerk responses to why they started drinking and using drugs as teenagers, concede that no one pressured them. No one pushed a drug at them. They were offered it, and if they refused, no one pressed the issue. Teasing, if any, took the friendliest form. Whatever pressure there was came from them not someone else.

Sure, there is pressure to drink when drinking is part of an initiation rite. There are fraternities and a few sport teams that have incorporated excessive drinking into a rite of passage. Seventeen year-old lacrosse players have initiated sixteen-year old rookie sophomores by shaving their heads and having them guzzle down a couple of pints of beer. Twenty-one year olds have been known to require nineteen year olds to play rapid ingestion games with toxic doses of booze as part of pledging for a fraternity. It speaks of delayed adolescence, and prolonged immaturity on the part of those who do it. It is a sign of cultural immaturity when adults dismiss it as "boys will be boys."

"Just Say No"? The unfortunate result when parents persist in believing that their children face pressure from their peers is that they arm their children with "peer resistance education." This approach has proven not only to be a failure, but one which at the same time demonizes their son's and daughter's friends. Some evil little twelve-year old is out there trying to get your sixth grader drunk.

If our culture drifts toward paranoia, it will be more the result of our own use of toxic substances, our sense that predators are everywhere, and our tendency to place blame rather than seek to understand others and their motives. The irony of "Just Say No" is that a teen ends up having to say "No" to a part of him that has "Just Said Yes."

Middle School Drinking and Drunking: The simple and uncomplicated truth is that middle-school youngsters drink out of curiosity and peer acceptance. They heard it "makes you feel good," and they want to belong. That is not why they get drunk. They get drunk out of ignorance, youthful exuberance, or a combination of the two. They are unfamiliar with the dose–response equation and get drunk by accident. Either that or they want to feel like Superman. Or Wonder Woman? If a twelve-year old gets drunk for any other reason, his or her parents ought to be concerned. The reasons an older adolescent drinks and gets drunk are different. He has found his place in the peer social culture. He knows the dose-response equation.

Drinking in Older Adolescents: Older adolescents drink for some or all of the following reasons:

- It is social.
- It decreases inhibition.
- It's sophisticated - macho.
- It's a break from pressure.
- It's pleasurable. It's fun.

In other words, there are sixteen, seventeen, and eighteen year olds drink for pretty much the same reasons adults drink.

One high school senior, when asked about drinking among his group of friends, responded this way. "Parents don't seem to believe that some of us drink socially; we have a few beers with our friends at a party. Most of us are going to grow up to be social drinkers. Not all of us are interested in getting drunk, sick, throwing up, and tearing a house apart." Admittedly, this young man was more mature than a good many of his peers, but he is not as rare as one might think.

The statistics should concern us for sure. According to an ongoing study, Monitoring The Future, conducted by The University of Michigan (at http://www.monitoringthefuture.org), data for 2006 indicates that: 3% of high school seniors drink daily; 1.6% have been drunk daily; and 26.5% have participated in binge drinking. (Binge drinking is defined as having five or more drinks on one occasion within the past two weeks.) Put simply, it is quite possible that 3% or more of the class of 2006 is already alcoholic.

Monitoring the Future statistics also show that 45.3% of the Class of 2006 used alcohol in the month prior to the survey, and that 30% of graduating seniors had gotten drunk that month. But as troubling as that statistic is, it also indicates that: 15% (about one-third of those who did drink the prior month) did not get drunk that month; 55 of every 100 seniors (more than half) did not even drink alcohol that month; and even though 30 out of 100 did get drunk, the majority, 70 of the 100, did not.

Parents are concerned that their children will drink alcohol at a time when they are supposed to be learning who they are and what they want to be, at a time when they are supposed to connect with others and learn how to socialize. Parents are concerned that their children are loading a brain yet to be fully matured with a toxin. They are concerned that drinking is not a healthy way to grow and develop, and that drinking is going to interfere with important developmental tasks.

There are only three important questions a teenager must answer before he enters the adult world, "Who am I? Where am I going? And who will go with me?" Equal in importance to knowing what those questions are, is knowing never to answer them in reverse order. Before a kid decides who will accompany him in his journey through life, he had better decide first where *he* is going, and hope that where *he* is going is based in some way on *who* he is. Kids who are involved with alcohol and drugs hang with other kids who are involved with alcohol and drugs. They answer the questions backwards. And so a kid ends up deciding who he is based on who he hangs with.

Parents are concerned about their kid's drinking, but what really frightens them is that kids take foolish and potentially fatal risks under the influence. High school juniors and seniors will occasionally drink excessively on purpose as do adults. And anyone who drinks alcohol takes a risk, not just kids and alcoholics. Alcohol is not selective in whom it kills. It kills young people and adults. It kills alcoholics and non-alcoholics alike. What terrifies parents most is the thought that they may lose a child to drunking.

Why Drunk?   Why do older adolescents get drunk? The reason often involves one or more of the following:

- Those who started drinking late may get drunk as do younger kids because they lack dose experience.

- Sometimes the driving force is "testosterone." It's about "Being the Man" as one high school senior put it.

- For a particular youngster getting drunk at a party may have become his way of standing out from the ordinary. Getting drunk gives him panache. Regrettably, there are kids for whom getting drunk seems to be the social role they play. Alcoholic or not, this reason ought to concern his parents.

- For a few teenagers, addiction is the reason they get drunk. In other words, they can't keep from drunking.

But that's the minority of cases. Most upper school students *drunk* for four reasons:

- Teenagers imitate adults, and getting drunk has become a way of intense celebrating in our culture. For teens it becomes a way of celebrating or even creating intense, meaningful, and transitional experiences. It is a way to rejoice that your team won. It is a way to have something to remember later on.

- For boys and young men getting drunk together is a way of bonding, a way to be close to each other. It gives them permission to share feelings which are ordinarily prohibited to males.

- Some end of high school and college drunking is a kind of "Last Hurrahing," a way to say so long to old friends, goodbye to school, and farewell to the carefree days.

- Sometimes getting drunk gives a young man or woman permission to act out sexually with impunity.

These are some powerful forces. Some are understandably human; others poignantly so. Some of the motives point to disturbing flaws in our culture. When kids get roaring drunk to celebrate a championship, they are imitating what adults have done in a town that won a league or national championship. If sharing feelings while sober from male to male runs the risk of sexual ridicule, then our cultural attitude toward masculinity and feelings is itself adolescent. If pre-graduation drunking is a farewell to fun, we might wonder how deadly boring we have suggested growing up is. For example, we have all heard graduates say, "I guess we'll have to be adults now."

The gulf between the "world of college" and the "world of work" has grown wider and wider. Although the issue is debatable, young adults between the ages 21 and 28 may be having more than the usual difficulty navigating it. St. Elmo's Fire is a movie that portrays the transition compassionately. Even though its debut was years ago in 1985, the movie speaks to young adults more than twenty years later. Two years earlier, The Big Chill (1983) chronicled the trials and tribulations of young adults who had just survived the transition, some not so well and one not at all. The popularity of the TV show, Thirty-Something, had to be tied to the possibility that it spoke as much to a Twenty-Something audience, longing to connect to peers. If we had the statistics, they might show that more youngsters are entering college later and graduating later than did their parents a generation ago. Some of whom may have actually benefited from entering later. The Partnership for a Drug-Free America in April of 2007 devoted several web pages to addressing concerns of parents whose 18 to 25 year olds are drinking and getting drunk in scary ways and well past graduation. (http://www.drugfree.org/). Sadly, college drinking may not end at graduation.

Anyone who takes the time to think about the motives youngsters have for getting drunk will recognize that they are not mysterious. Teenagers are not another species; they're human. And although their motives are not always the noblest (sexual acting out), they are within the scope of human understanding (celebrating), and some speak to powerful human needs (bonding). Parents may not approve of the means used to achieve the ends, but they can understand the ends if they think about it.

What About Girls? As a rule, girls do not get drunk as do boys in large boisterous groups without the opposite sex. Although no one should be surprised if such behavior arrives on the scene, as in some arenas and areas it may already have. As yet, society is shocked if a large group of girls gets drunk and rowdy, and proceeds to destroy a sorority house. We have not yet reached the point where "girls will be girls" is as common an American idiom as "boys will be boys." But no one should wonder why young women who want parity with males, who work to tone muscular bodies, who compete in "extreme boxing," who play in the same sports arenas as males, and who go after top paying and powerful jobs, will mistake being "equal to men" as being "like men." That men and women are equal does not mean that they are the same. For example, four plus four equals eight. But so do seven plus one; six plus two; and five plus three.

Some girls do get drunk in pairs or threes, which should concern parents if it has become the girl's regular way of socializing. (It should also concern parents when pairs of boys do it.) And if getting drunk together that way has become their exclusive way of socializing – that points to the need for intervention.

When girls do get drunk, they generally do so with the boys because getting drunk with the boys is a way to connect with boys, a way to be accepted, to relate, and to be "in" with them.

On the other hand, drinking for girls seems to happen for pretty much the same reasons as it does for boys:

- It is social.

- It decreases inhibition.

- It's sophisticated - sexy.

- It's a break from pressure.

- It's pleasurable. It's fun.

A group of girls had been brought together to discuss why girls in their peer group drink and smoke. One girl from the group put it this way, and her inflection priceless. She said, "Well man, it's about *looking good*." Her intent was unmistakable. For some girls, drinking is all about looking sexy, mature, and sophisticated. A sixteen-year old young woman with a drink in one hand and a cigarette in the other feels very sexy and adult-like.

Teenagers learn early on that being female is defined by shaping an appearance and that being male is defined by developing a personality. It is more important for a boy to be "rugged" and a girl to have "a figure." And so it is little wonder that one side benefit for nicotine use among girls is weight control.

Finally, one of the roles girls play in the socializing game is to take care of the boys when the boys get drunk. It appeals to the maternal instinct in them.

Why Drugs?   It is a colossal mistake to think that kids who fool around with psychoactive drugs are lonely, isolated, disturbed, abused, crazy, psychologically tentative, weird, wanting to escape reality, and in the minority. According to the statistics for 2006 (cf. Monitoring The Future), by the end of eighth grade more than one in five have used *any* illicit drug at least once, and nearly half of all twelfth graders have tried one. Over the four years of high school, kids perceive marijuana as easier to get and as decreasingly risky. This is confirmed by the number of those who over the high school years try that drug: 15.7% in eighth grade, 31.8% in tenth grade, and 42.3% by twelfth grade. In the month prior to being surveyed, for every 100 students, 8.1% of eighth graders, 16.8% of tenth graders, and 21.5% of twelfth graders had used *any* illicit drug. Marijuana and hashish topped the list. Some years ago, alcohol and marijuana became a familiar duo as drugs of abuse. In fact, one curious statistic reveals that more twelfth graders use marijuana than use alcohol daily (3% using alcohol and 5% using marijuana daily).

So why do kids drug? The answer is that it depends on the kid and the drug. The goal for parents, therapists, and counselors is to tease out which reason applies to which adolescent. The list of motives is long, and sometimes curious, but often understandable. And if we look beyond the means (risky drug use) to see the purpose and the goal (what kids are trying to gain), we see in some instances that their motives suggest the exercise of skills and the development of character traits necessary to adult life. Things can seem either disturbing or understandable depending on how you say it. The words matter.

Reasons kids use drugs are:

- Curiosity – An inquisitive spirit.
- Boundary testing - Testing one's power.
- Belonging to a gang – Affiliation. Being part of the crowd.
- Defiance and rebelliousness - Assertion of independence.
- Thrill seeking – Urge for vitality and life.
- Escape from painful feeling and painful circumstances.
- Addiction.

Again, the method may cause parents no small amount of annoyance, chagrin, and fear. But a parent cannot deny that the motives are understandable, and fundamentally human. Some motives are essential for growth, while others are praiseworthy. Surely, as a country, we do not want a nation of drug addicts. But we cannot remain strong if our children grow up timid, dull, frightened, content, isolated, dependent, completely and passively compliant either. We need men and women who are curious, willing to push the limits, adventurous, eager to discover, strong, confident, vibrant and full of energy. America was not built by men and women who played games in front of computer screens.

Teaching kids about psychoactive drugs, the symptoms of addiction, and the risks they take when they use them is only part of teen drug abuse prevention. Equally important are programs which provide youngsters opportunities to push limits, explore new experiences, feel vibrant and alive, bond with their peers, and assert their power and independence without the dangerous risks of drug use.

Kids want to have fun, be sociable, explore their feelings, put inhibition aside for a moment, "chill" after two tests and a term paper, express strong feelings, socialize with the opposite sex, have friends, act goofy, bond, and connect with others in meaningful ways. Helping them find safe ways to do it ought to be at least half of our drug-abuse prevention efforts.

Advice for Parents: Make no mistake; the style of drug use today is different from a time parents remember. In the 1960s and 1970s, drugs were part of a counter-culture. They were associated with flamboyant individualism and freedom. A political stance fueled it; it was coupled with an Anti-War Movement. Its motto was "Love, Peace and Understanding." It was part and parcel of liberation and non-violent resistance, as well as rebellion against prejudice, narrowness, and violence. It was out in the open. "Look at us" was the watchword at Woodstock. Flower children put daisies in the gun barrels of National Guard Troops.

Today a drug-dealing, drug-using kid is more likely to carry a gun. Equipped with a cell phone and a pager, and driving a snappy Sport Utility Vehicle, drug-involved kids are part of an underground society. Cops and robbers is their game; "Catch us if you can" is its motto. The game depends on an "us versus them" mentality on the part of the teenagers and adults involved. The struggle intensifies when adults put all their energies into playing cop. The conflict is fueled by what youngsters perceive to be the adult hypocrisy of condemning drug use while drinking alcohol. And it becomes destructive when all parties battle for control. This is the environment parents face today.

In such an environment, parents who hope to raise teenagers in ways that will help their children avoid or delay alcohol and drug use might take some of the following advice:

- Teach children facts. Don't try scaring them into compliance.

- Tell your sons and daughters that risk itself is not a bad thing, but that risks do have consequences. And the critical question is whether the potential gain exceeds what might be lost if one takes a risk and loses?

- Don't just tell kids that it is okay to make mistakes. Model that it is okay by admitting when you make them.

- Show kids how to have fun by having adult fun without alcohol.

- Express feelings. It is the loudest and clearest way to say it's okay to feel,   even publicly.

- Be sure your kids know that there is no problem they cannot bring to you.

- Help them discover that imagination is the best toy they have. Don't entertain them. Help them find ways to entertain themselves.

- Love them. Love makes it possible for us not to be afraid; it helps us avoid rationalizing our way out of taking responsibility for mistakes – love helps us be honest with ourselves.

- Be silly with them and let them be silly too.

Today, many parents chauffer their kids to soccer, ballet, music lessons, tutoring, travel leagues, and art class. Their lives are spent as spectators at the little league. Little leagues start when children are old enough to run, and the little team that wins may go on to compete at a regional, or perhaps national level. It is both exhausting and exhilarating.

Actually, all a group of parents has to do is get together and find an open field and a ball-shaped object and tell kids to make up a game. After a half hour, with just those ingredients, and after arguing about what they can and cannot do, their kids will have created a game along with boundaries and a set of rules. Not only will the kids have fun, they will have developed imagination and a set of social interaction skills necessary to adult life. When we rob kids of imagination, drugs become appealing.

When children see that the only time adults socialize is with alcohol, the message is clear.   Parents who express feelings sober and who get silly sober send a powerful message too. This does not preclude adult drinking. Kids need to learn too that there are different rules for adults and children, and that adults have earned the right and have the maturity to do some things that kids have yet to earn.

Growing up is not nearly as stressful for a kid whose parents present themselves as vulnerable to making mistakes. Consider the pressure on a youngster who has to live up to perfect, mistake-free parents. Consider the pressure on the parents. Parents who admit that they occasionally "blow it" give their children permission to admit when they have "blown it." If denial drives addiction, then learning self honesty early in life may help prevent, at least, its advanced stages.

Parents, who teach their children the symptoms of addiction, encourage fearless self honesty, and make it clear that there is nothing their children cannot bring to them, may do as much as they can to prevent drug involvement.

Youngster Already Involved but not Addicted: Faced with a youngster who has crossed the line and is already involved with alcohol and drugs, but not addicted to them, parents must get support and do their best at the following:

- Avoid the extremes of denial and hysteria.

- Not all problematic drug use is addiction. By the same token, the notion that drinking and drug use is merely a phase that kids will grow out of is a risky notion too. Alcoholics and addicts are not the only ones harmed, maimed or killed by alcohol and other drugs.

- Avoid acting out of fear. Most attempts at controlling a teenager are driven by their parents' fear. Scared parents act impulsively. Fear leads angry parents to manipulative lying. Deal with fear first.

- The most dangerous message is that drug use is inevitable, intolerable, unspeakable, and unforgivable.

- For adolescents, substance use is always a multi-faceted issue. It is a violation of the law and the parents' rules, a violation of trust, and a health issue. The object is not to choose between punishment and counseling, but to administer both punishment along with counseling and education.

- By all means get support. Connect with other parents. Talk to schools that have an enlightened approach to dealing with drug-using youngsters.

- Remember that the motives which drive teen drinking and drunking are not always pathological.

- Get professional help in determining a course of action if addiction is suspected. Treat addiction as a primary disease. Dealing with addicted youngsters is discussed in detail below.

"Drugs are evil" or "Soft drugs will always lead to hard drugs" are lies driven by understandable motives. Adults who communicate such notions hope that scare tactics will protect their children by delaying the onset of drug use. This is a noble motive and an understandable reaction to parental fear. But the message backfires. Children learn the truth. Drugs cannot think, and so they cannot be evil. And kids know that if every adult who had ever used, or even abused, marijuana as a college student in the 1970s had ended up a heroin addict in the 1990s, hospitals and treatment facilities would have patients knocking on their doors and spilling out of their windows. Simply put, you cannot tell a kid a lie on Monday and expect him to trust you on Tuesday.

Punishment: Inevitably, kids will push the limits, and punishment becomes the necessary response. Punishment is intended to teach. The associated pain simply reinforces the lesson and makes it memorable. Pain is not the purpose. One dear grandmother put it this way, "At some point, if you can't listen you have to feel."

When it comes to punishment, an angry parent can find it difficult to avoid revenge as the motive and pain its purpose. And so being in touch with one's own feelings is an important first step for parents in the matter. Parents need to take time to process their feelings. In fact, the parent who lets his kid know the feelings behind a punishment teaches a powerful lesson by doing so. Parents are angry. They feel guilty about how little they can control their kids. They are ashamed of what their own peers might think. They are frustrated. They are hurt. They are sad. But most of all, they are scared. They are frightened by what might have happened to a kid who has gotten drunk. If a youngster sees only his parents' anger, he is likely to counter-attack. When kids learn that mom and dad were scared, and that their punishment is meant to teach, it is a bit easier to take. After all, a kid doesn't know how to counter-attack fear. Show him only anger and you're in for a fight.

Guidelines for Punishment

- Punishment must sting. A punishment that does not sting ends up telling a kid that his offense is trivial.

- If a kid doesn't know the reason for his punishment, he sees vengeance as the reason. The reason is simple; punishment is meant to teach.

- Because it is meant to teach, a punishment is best if coupled with some sort of educational prong. A youngster who abuses a drug ought to be required to learn the risks of abusing that drug.

- At the time of the punishment, an end date ought to be communicated to the youngster so that he knows his punishment will not last forever.

- A smart parent couples an end date with what a youngster can do in order to get his case reconsidered, and his punishment shortened or modified. In other words, parents are well-advised to set a review date, a point at which they will re-evaluate the case. It helps a kid avoid feeling helpless and angry. And that is why it is important that the youngster know what he can do to help that reconsideration tilt in his favor. For example, a parent could say something like this:

"We will reconsider your punishment in a month. If at that time you have apologized to those you have hurt, improved your Algebra grade, kept your room clean, and talked to us about school, life, and your friends, we may shorten, lighten or end the punishment."

Adolescents, who are punished for life, and powerless to do anything to change their fate, feel provoked to act out. That's when they crawl out of windows after dark or text message their friends about what ogres their parents are. That's when they break things and brood at dinner. That's when they displace their anger and kick cats and kid brothers. Many a parent has learned that grounding his son for life with absolutely no break ends up being perversely masochistic. Who is punished when all a kid can do is sit, brood, glare, and do homework he hates? Brief breaks, with the emphasis on brief, helps a kid understand that his parents are capable of compassion. Five minutes on the phone, ten minutes of instant messaging, or a brief play station break can take the pressure to act out off the kid. It helps parents endure the punishment as well.

Sensible parents never tie their hands; locking themselves into a
sentence they cannot commute (a punishment they cannot change)
without losing their authority. Wise parents know that punishment
and love are not mutually exclusive. A parent's continuing resentment will keep him from hugging his kid. Let it go. Punishment
isn't hatred. Hug him.

Parents who partner with schools may find important allies there.
Principals, teachers and counselors are parents too. They understand
how frustrating and anxiety-provoking the teen years can be, and
how tempting drugs and alcohol have become in our culture. In fact,
if you exclude time for sleeping, schools often have kids for as many
hours as parents.

The Parent – School Interface: School is often the first place
                                          society looks when education is
proposed as the answer to teen substance abuse. Schools have been
asked to add health education, with a unit on drugs and alcohol, to
their current curriculum of Spanish, calculus, history, English, and
biology. The pressure increases exponentially when anxious and
burdened parents demand that schools "do something." And the
drug and alcohol solution dead-ends in one of two ways: 1) either a
school satisfies its obligation by putting on a big show and inviting an
NFL linebacker to address a school-wide assembly on the dangers of
drugs; or 2) the school counters with *"the problem belongs at home with
parents and in the courts with police, not with teachers and classrooms."*
Either the school puts on a program that looks good, or one part of
the social circle points to the others as responsible for spear-heading
the solution.

Schools might be an ally in dealing with a kid who has gotten involved in using alcohol and other drugs. A counselor or teacher may
prove an adult voice that a kid can hear more readily than he can hear
his parent. Parents, then, do need to learn their school's stance on alcohol and other drug issues. Some schools will help. Others abdicate
their responsibility to educate when they adopt a "One Strike" policy
(i.e., one offense means expulsion). The sign over the entrance says
"School," not Courtroom, Detention Center, Mental Health Clinic, or

Boot Camp. Schools with a "One-Strike" policy shut themselves off as a resource for worried parents looking for an ally.   In fact, if a school is adept at catching all its current drug users and expels every one of them, including of course alcohol drinkers, the school will find itself graduating less than half the senior class that entered in the fall.

School - The Fear Free Zone: School cannot be expected to tolerate all teenage behavior and accomplish its educational mission at the same time. The one thing a school cannot tolerate is fear. No one can learn if there is imminent danger in the environment. Scared and in a defensive and protective posture, a youngster is neither ready nor able to hear or incorporate information and ideas. The one circumstance in which a single offense is grounds for expulsion is when that offense introduces fear within the walls of the school. Other than fear, a school's job is to take every opportunity it faces to educate. That includes implementing a tough and compassionate policy of intervention, punishment, education, counseling and referral for alcohol and/or drug offenses.   Parents who are dealing with a child who is using drugs need to know what their school's "program" is.

Other factors complicate the solution for both schools and parents. Twenty years ago researchers were already concluding that school educational programs were having little impact on behavior. In a meta-analysis, a statistical procedure which allows comparisons to be made among different statistical studies, researchers at the University of Albany integrated the outcomes of thirty-three evaluations of school educational programs. The meta-analysis shows that education has its most positive effect on knowledge and attitudes, but has been essentially unsuccessful in changing the drug-using behavior of students (Bangert-Drowns, 1988). Other sorts of educational programs, including peer education, have shown promise. However, adult led, didactic programs may change the way a kid thinks about drugs for a little while, but they do little to change the way he acts.

We move further from a solution when the language of community meetings and parent teacher gatherings devolves into rhetorical extremes. From, "It's a phase, relax" to "It's a crime; lock them up; kick 'em out."

Parents can ally with schools that have an enlightened view of their responsibility to educate while recognizing that education, counseling and referral and not addiction treatment is that responsibility. Parents looking for support should

- Get involved. Be a helper to your children's school, not one of its critics.

- Support programs aimed at changing behavior and creating a shift in cultural mores. The "Big Show" impresses kids at the time, but fails to change what the kids do on the weekend. A student drug education program that does little more than communicate information will often find that the kids have heard the information a dozen times already. A kid may have a head full of information about the nature of alcohol, but that knowledge does him little good if he gets into the driver's seat drunk.

- Volunteer to help your community run programs that provide an alternative to alcohol and drug use, and programs that promote attractive activities that integrate teen input. Teen centers and youth center dances disappeared some time ago. Finding programs that will attract sixteen year olds is a daunting task; it requires adult patience, imagination and effort. It takes parents who are willing to set it up and step aside - out of obvious sight. Parents and teachers who stand arms-folded on the sidelines make boys and girls feel very child-like when they are trying to feel very adult-like.

School-Based Educational Programs: School-based programs of drug abuse prevention have taken several directions, which address a range of audiences with a variety of purposes. Some schools have taken on the task of educating both students and their parents. Schools that accept parental education as their responsibility often find that a college information night is likely to draw ten times as many parents as will post for a drug information evening. When a drug education program follows a community tragedy, like the death of a youngster in a drunken driving incident, adult attendance peaks. But the energy for action and broad-based involvement is short-lived, and sooner or later, the busyness of life and denial replaces fear. Parents lead busy lives. They are not immune to denial. It is comforting to think that "this won't happen to our family." Keeping parents engaged requires creating programs that involve parents interacting with each other, not just sitting and listening to experts belabor the obvious, or asking parents to sign pledges that they will not make alcohol available to kids in their homes.

Putting on The School's Alcohol and Drug Awareness - Prevention Show for students looks good. It satisfies parents that a dramatic and powerful message has been put before their children. But, besides the fact that The Big Show has little impact on behavior, putting on the program often saps the best energy of the most devoted teachers and counselors and exhausts them. In fact, the result of putting it on leads organizers to feel that they have responded to social and parental pressure and satisfied their drug education responsibility for the year.

A good teacher knows that a lesson is more effective when it is reinforced in a dozen little ways over time. Drug and alcohol education is quite easily incorporated into a Chemistry class and can blend seamlessly into an English literature class. Education can happen silently with wall posters that are imaginative, powerful, funny, and eye catching. This is especially so when changed frequently as well. Drug and alcohol education is more effective if it comes not just from the Counseling staff, but from the Principals Office, the Health Suite, and the History Department. A favorite teacher can have a life-changing influence. And the Athletic Department may have more power to influence the choices kids make about alcohol and drug use than any other single group in the school. Getting coaches involved in the process is invaluable, especially for girls and boys involved in sports.

Educational programs for students have been a mixed bag, each with its own goal and philosophical underpinnings. Some programs hope to delay the onset of drug use and hire motivational speakers to that end. Others shock kids, hoping they will be frightened into compliance. Cognitively based programs educate the mind with the belief that if a kid thinks drugs are dangerous, he will not try them. Peer Resistance Education, based on the erroneous premise that pressure drives drug use, teaches kid how to "Just Say No."

Peer Education: In Baltimore, Maryland, Tom and Pam O'Neil, parents of a bright and energetic high school junior who died in what is mistakenly called an accident; put their grief and their energy into Peer Education. With the help of Dr. Charles Deutsch of The Harvard School of Public Health, teachers and counselors in more than a dozen Baltimore private and Catholic schools train sophomore, junior and senior students to help younger kids talk about alcohol and drugs and other topics determined by the individual school. Anecdotes from student peer educators and their adult mentors tell the story of a committed group excited by what they see and hear in classrooms time and time again.

The premise is that younger kids listen to the guys and girls who are just a little older than themselves. They see their peers, not just their parents, as role models. Teams of student peer educators get kids talking not just listening. They encourage the younger kids "to get real." There is not a single Baltimore school that has dropped Peer Education Program once they started it. Faculty members who have been involved in this program for as many as fifteen years come into it each year with enthusiasm. They do not burn out.

Parent to Parent School Programs: Parent to parent programs choose parents as the target audience. Programs that create opportunities for face to face, parent to parent meetings are more effective than lectures. Initiatives that ask parents to sign a pledge that theirs are safe homes are not as effective as parents meeting face to face to discuss how they can cooperate in reinforcing their rules.

The day his son or daughter enters ninth grade, a kid-friendly parent adopts a bunch of surrogate children, his child's friends. Parents need to talk to each other about their hopes, guidelines, desires and fears. They need to get past the awkwardness of being open with each other about stuff that feels personal. Parents who do not talk to other parents are likely to hear their kids say "you're the only parents who do not allow....." The kids are networking, and their parents ought to do the same. Effective networking is not done on paper; it is done in person. Schools can help provide the time and place for this to happen.

Youngsters Already Addicted: There is no junior version of addiction, only the adult diagnosis. Youngsters, even before they are thirteen, can and do, match its criteria. Diagnosing addiction in an adolescent is no easy task, however. It is complicated by the adolescent culture, adolescent motivation, denial, and immaturity.

Diagnosing Addiction in an Adolescent

What is involved in diagnosing addiction in an adolescent entails determining whether *real* loss of control exists and not simply isolated instances of drunkenness. Loss of control is not to be equated with acute intoxication. People, including kids, may become acutely intoxicated in one of three ways: accidentally, intentionally or unintentionally. Loss of control is unintended acute intoxication which has persisted as a pattern over time, which is not to be confused with getting drunk. The unfortunate complication in the adolescent world is that intoxication becomes the name of the game. They want to get drunk. Is a kid getting drunk because he wants to or because he has lost control? Teasing this out is the heart of the matter and not easy.

An addiction diagnosis requires clear evidence that tolerance has developed. It is often impossible to tell whether a kid is bragging about his capacity or has developed *true* tolerance. A single night of heavy drinking does not prove tolerance. Tolerance is the ability to withstand high doses without apparent effect. Thus, an evening of drinking and getting sick is not it.

Diagnosing addiction in an adolescent requires that one determine that the youngster persists in drinking and/or drug use despite recurring problems because a compulsive force is at work, and not just adolescent partying, immaturity and risk taking. All too often, there is just not enough history to conclude that a real compulsive force is at work.

Diagnosing addiction in a youngster is not impossible, however. And when addiction is the problem, parents need to aim in the direction of treated abstinence as the ultimate goal. The youngster who volunteers to enter treatment is an ideal; expecting it is unrealistic. Denial is strong in addicts, and when the ordinary denial that comes from being an adolescent accompanies it, the problem increases by more than a power or two.

Pencil and paper tests will not always tell one the answers to the three pronged criteria for addiction in the case of youngsters. Therefore, some end up falling into that gray area somewhere between abuse and addiction.

A Progressive-Intensive Treatment Contract

A youngster may cooperate in entering a treatment center, but more often, getting a youngster to engage involves a step by step move in that direction. One approach involves a progressive-intensive treatment contract in which a youngster agrees to a lower level intervention. And if or when he fails to stay clean and sober, he agrees to up the intensity of his treatment. Parents who try this approach must individualize it to suit their child. The elements and their sequence will differ from case to case. A progressive-intensive contract might include the following. The preliminary step is to get the youngster to see that it is reasonable to see at least a period of abstinence is a necessary part of the process, which is no easy task. Someone intoxicated is unable to figure out whether he has a problem, or if he suspects that he does have a problem, drinking makes it impossible for him to deal with it. Once abstinent, the youngster agrees to remain abstinent on the basis of one to one counseling. If individual counseling fails, he agrees to go to Alcoholics Anonymous or Narcotics Anonymous and/or to add Antabuse. If that fails, he will enter a formal outpatient program. And if that fails, he will go to inpatient treatment. This approach hopes to convince the youngster that it is not his parent's whim but his behavior that drives the process. Simply put, the reason more intensive treatment is necessary is because a lesser approach fails.

Fear and the Illusion of Control

The parents of an addicted adolescent know all too well what emotion drives them. Fear. Fear that they will lose a child. That fear is what leads parents to all sorts of manipulations, supervision, and attempts at controlling their youngster's behavior. Parents search the field of professionals hoping to find someone who has a guaranteed approach to safety, twenty-four/seven. Only eyeball observation every minute of the day will accomplish that sort of control. The product of attempting such control is that it leads to battles for control. Either the youngster wins, or he uses the battle as an excuse to drink and drug and blame his parents for it.

A parent can guide, advise, counsel, encourage, support, love, and even warn, a child. Parents can set limits and enforce consequences if those limits are violated. But the truth is that, after a certain age, parents cannot make their children think what they want them to think, feel what they want them to feel, or do what they want them to do.

Life allows a parent the illusion of control until a youngster is about twelve or thirteen years old. After that the illusion fades. Parents do not have to let go of control because they don't have control. What they have to let go of is the illusion of control. Letting go of that illusion, however, is probably the single most difficult task a parent is asked to face when his son or daughter is addicted. And to try letting go without support from an understanding community and without a program of intervention in place is sure to make the process near impossible. Fear of the potential consequences is too great.

A Cultural Solution: Abuse of and addiction to alcohol and/or other drugs among teenagers are not a regional issue. The problem is cultural, with significant economic and international complications. No school program, no one speech, no famous role model, no single law, no public service announcement, no program of interdiction, and no imaginative poster alone are going to change it. It will require a broad based and systematic approach with as much emphasis on a cultural change of mind as on local and national, privately and publicly funded programs of education, intervention, incarceration, prevention, punishment, and treatment.

If as a culture we help kids get past posturing and spouting macho rhetoric, we will move in the direction of a culture shift. If we show kids a way to be "real" with each other, we will help them gain confidence. If we model self honesty, we will show them that self honesty is admirable, mature, and powerful. If we provide kids opportunities to talk to each other honestly and candidly about growing up, we will help them find friends. If we provide a time and a place for young people to experience the thrill of being alive without chemical stimulation, we will move toward a healthy society. If sometimes adults party without alcohol, they will model for children that alcohol is only one way to party. It will model a behavior that is healthy for both. If we hope to change the attitudes and behaviors of our kids, we may first have to change our own attitudes and behaviors.

12

THE FAMILY'S ILLNESS

Calling alcoholism a family illness could mean that alcoholism runs in families. And it does. It could mean that individuals may be born pre-disposed to developing an alcohol problem. This is also true. However, what is meant most often when addiction is called a family illness is that those who live with alcoholics and other addicts get sick too. They can get as sick emotionally as alcoholics themselves. Sometimes they can even get sicker. From the beginning, Alcoholics Anonymous recognized that, to a certain extent, "the entire family of an alcoholic is ill" (AA, 1976, p. 122). For family members who never drank, this is hard to take. Having put up with active alcoholism, one is hardly flattered to be called sick and in need of help at the start of recovery.

The Mathematics of a Family's Illness: Getting sick from living with alcoholism is practically unavoidable. The forces at work on individuals are multiple and powerful. When added together, their impact is considerable. To escape the experience unaffected would be miraculous.

Living with an alcoholic is to live with his symptoms and to do so for a long time. It is to live with denial, guilt, anger, fear, shame, and sadness. Trusting an alcoholic is to trust someone whose thinking is drug distorted. Trying to help an addict is to find that one's best efforts have little or no effect, and at times, even seem to make matters worse. It is confusing and frustrating to say the least.

Living with Symptoms: A person dying from a terminal illness, such as cancer, experiences some very powerful emotions like sadness, anger, and fear. Living with these feelings affects members of his family. The family who lives with a degenerative mental illness lives with strange behavior, and that behavior affects the family too. The family of an alcoholic lives with both. It is a disease capable of killing its victim without notice, and it is a disease which produces disturbing behavioral and psychological symptoms. The impact is predictable.

The range and intensity of an alcoholic's symptoms are phenomenal. He is drunk, moody, unpredictable, suicidal, manipulative, rageful, resentful, ashamed, guilty, fearful and terrified. He is as suddenly explosive as he is unexpectedly gentle. He may be abusive physically and emotionally. His love and neglect are equally unpredictable. An alcoholic's family is exposed to nearly every symptom in the psychiatric textbooks as well as an addict's physical health problems. When addicts are drug-poisoned or in withdrawal, family members witness psychotic behavior, delusions, hallucinations, and paranoia.

The Impact of a Long History: The family of a cancer patient may live with the pain of that problem for several years. But alcoholic families live with that problem for ten, twenty, even thirty or more years, and do so without knowing that they are living with a disease. Not only is stress cumulative, the insidiousness of chemical dependency is that families live with its pathology for so long that pathology seems the normal state of affairs. And in more than a few cases, the person who is supposed to be sick looks quite well and even at times is accorded respect from the world in which he works.

It is common for children of alcoholics to grow up accepting unusual and bizarre behavior as if it were normal. A teenager whose father's tolerance for booze was enormous was sixteen years old before he realized that most men can not consume a fifth of whiskey in an evening and still hold a coherent conversation. His father could. Addicts and alcoholics are famous for "crashing." In such homes, children awaken to find strangers sprawled all over the living room floor asleep, their home regularly invaded by a father's, brother's, sister's, or mother's drinking buddies. These children grow up with little privacy and less sense of their right to it. They live in homes without boundaries. And if the alcoholic parent is magnanimous and the non-addicted parent nasty and vindictive, their confusion multiplies. Often enough, children in an alcoholic home are as disturbed by the behavior of their non-alcoholic parent, as they are to the alcoholic one. And there is more.

Living with Denial and Blame: Cancer patients do not blame their loved ones for causing cancer. Alcoholics do blame others, and family members come in for a major share of that blame. An addict's denial affects his or her family members, causing them to doubt their perceptions and their ability to interpret events occurring around them. It erodes their self-confidence and self esteem. Either directly or by innuendo the addict's message to his family is that it is their fault. If they were somehow different, he would not be as he is and do what he does. An alcoholic's spouse may have been told many times that if she "were a better wife, more affectionate, sexier, a better lover, cook, provider, or companion," things would be different, and he would not look for companionship elsewhere. Alcoholics have accused their spouses of being cold, cruel, stupid, ugly, insensitive, phony and unloving. Anyone who is told repeatedly that he is stupid is affected by the criticism, and the damage doubles when it comes from a trusted source. A spouse thinks, "No one is closer to me. I have trusted him with my deepest thoughts. I can't ignore his opinion." This makes people sick, but there is more.

Living with Guilt: Alcoholism assaults self esteem on several fronts. For the family that does not accept chemical dependency as a disease, family members are easily persuaded into thinking that they have caused it and quite naturally feel guilty about that. Family members judge themselves as cruel, incompetent, worthless, vicious and powerful, all at the same time. But family guilt and shame result not only from an addict's accusations toward them. An extra helping of those feelings result from their own rage, bitterness, hatred, and even murderous feelings. Finally, it is impossible to maintain self-esteem if you feel not only that you have caused a problem but also that you are powerless to do anything about it. And that feeling is garden variety for alcoholic families. Each time the family fails to get its alcoholic loved one sober, members feel powerless and impotent, and even more determined to try harder next time. There's more.

Living with Anger: Frustration, hurt, broken trust and miscommunication are common triggers for anger. If so, living with alcoholics provides ample opportunities for anger. It does not, however, provide healthy models for dealing with anger. One of alcoholism's many ironies is that family members learn to deal with their anger in the same way addicts deal with theirs, either by stuffing it or blowing it.

There is little wonder why the husband, wife, or the children of an addict stuff their anger. They have good reasons to. A child who is told repeatedly that he is stupid begins to believe it if the teller is someone he trusts. To express anger, however, one must believe he has rights. In fact, anger is at times just that, an expression of one's rights. But family members who believe they are stupid, guilty, or incompetent, quite naturally presume that they have no right to be angry. "Who am I to find fault with others?" And so anger is either stuffed or denied. Even when a family member believes his anger is justified, he or she is still afraid to express it because the price he or she will have to pay (the emotional isolation, abuse, or abandonment), is too high. There is more.

Living with Fear: Alcoholic families live with the triple fears of abuse, abandonment and death. The impact is far reaching. The elderly parents of a young marijuana addict would regularly awaken in the middle of the night to see if the gas stove had been left on because their son's habit was to come home late, fix something to eat, and forget to turn the stove off. More than once they found the downstairs filled with smoke. And if the phone rang when their son was out, fear immobilized them, never sure what the call might mean. There is more.

Enabling and Its Frustrations: Enablers serve addicts in several ways. They rescue them from jams. They help them deny their addiction. They cover up its consequences. If they nag, they provide drinkers and druggers an excuse to drink and/or drug and someone to blame it on as well.

Enabling is not an act of stupidity or cruelty. It is motivated by the understandable emotions of fear, guilt, love, and hope. Family members enable because they are afraid of what will happen if they do not. They enable hoping enabling will work, and that somehow it will help. They enable because they think they owe it – out of loyalty. They cover up for an alcoholic's drunken behavior to avoid its shame. They enable because they believe that somehow enabling shows they care. Occasionally, an individual family member enables because he or she benefits from enabling. In a family with two alcoholics one will enable the other in order to keep the focus off himself and hide behind another's problem. A parent who gets the respect of his or her children because he or she is long-suffering, noble and self-sacrificing finds it difficult to stop enabling and give up the admiration which comes as a result of it.

Family members do not think that their enabling helps addiction continue. They believe they are trying to get it to stop. They think that by rescuing they will stir up enough gratitude in an alcoholic for him to want to stop drinking. They think that by making excuses for him he will return the favor and act responsibly, or that by nagging they will wear him down, causing him to change. And when their efforts have little or no effect, or when their enabling make matters worse, families are frustrated, frightened, and all the more desperate to control. Enabling is exhausting. There is more.

Responsibility without Control: Those who live with someone who is out of control will almost instinctively respond by taking control or trying to. Family members assume responsibility for all sorts of things, such as keeping an alcoholic in a good mood, managing his drunkenness, scheduling social life around him, taking care of the household, and managing the atmosphere so as not to provoke drinking or drugging. Family members assume responsibility for explaining an alcoholic's behavior to others, protecting others from his abuse, and preventing fatal consequences when he is drunk. Individual members assume responsibility for entire families, reasoning that if someone doesn't take charge, disaster is sure to follow. The problem is that all the while a family member strives for control, he or she realizes at some level that he has neither the power nor the means to control. The knot in one's stomach is so often the result when people feel both responsible and powerless, and that knot doesn't go away until one learns what Al-Anon calls "letting go."

"Sometimes Sicker": At treatment facilities it is the custom to introduce new patients and accompanying family members to the staff members who are on duty at the time of admission. At one facility on one such occasion, one staff member missed the introductions. When he finally met the couple, he was astonished at how weakened and exhausted the man was, certain that his withdrawal would be difficult and that it would be days before this poor man would recover from the beating alcoholism had given him. The staff member had made one mistake. The man was not the patient. His wife was. Her husband was exhausted from the tasks of living with an addict. In another instance, a woman accompanied her husband the morning of his admission, a day on which she had scheduled a business appointment for herself later that afternoon. During the admitting process she managed to smile and perform in a business-like manner until her husband was taken off for his physical examination. No sooner had he left the room, than she turned to the staff and said, "I hope someone here finally gives it to that son-of-a-bitch." With that she marched down the hall and had gotten halfway when she stopped and turned around. With tears streaming down her face, she said to the staff member who had followed her, "Please apologize to those people for me. I'm sorry. I just don't know what I feel anymore."

Al-Anon and Nar-Anon: Families who fail to get help for themselves remain governed by confusing emotions and motivations, often unconsciously so. Reading books and attending lectures about addiction helps, but insight is usually not enough. Minds need information. That is certain, but pain is at another level, and it is feeling which must heal. Family recovery is the goal of Al-Anon and Nar-Anon, organizations that have helped many. These groups are most helpful, however, when one goes to them for the right person and for the right reason. Alcoholics do not recover because their families attend Al-Anon meetings. Addicts do not stop using drugs because their parents go to Nar-Anon. It is the family who gets well at Al-Anon and Nar-Anon. The husband of an alcoholic makes his first mistake if he thinks Al-Anon will teach him how to get his wife sober. He makes his second mistake if he believes that his own emotional well-being depends on her recovering.

Recovery for a family commences when its members accept that they have something to recover from. The axiom of recovery is as true for the family as it is for the alcoholic. In order to get well, one must first be sick. The toughest part about getting well is admitting you need to.

Al-Anon can be helpful in two situations, living with an active alcoholic and living with a recovering one. Some Al-Anon members wonder which of those situations is the more difficult.

Coping with An Active Addict: Living with addiction is frustrating, frightening, painful, and disturbing. It is not, however, impossible. At this moment family members are living with surprising equanimity because they have learned a few of the principles that guide self help groups.

There is, of course, no foolproof recipe for getting an alcoholic sober. There are "Do's" and "Don'ts" which might persuade an alcoholic to enter treatment and at the same time provide some peace of mind for his family.

<u>Do</u>	<u>Don't</u>
Detach	**Ask Why**
Live Life	**Bluff**
Concentrate on Self	**Enable**
Confront with Love	**Be the Cure**

Detach

To survive in an alcoholic environment, a family must learn not to blame itself for causing the alcoholic's disease or the behavior it produces. Al-Anon members learn three **Cs**: "you can't *Cause* it; you can't *Control* it, and you can't *Cure* it." Detachment means internalizing those three **Cs**.

Detachment does not mean sitting silently by and watching a loved one get sicker and sicker until he hits bottom. It does not mean that someone is supposed to stop loving and stop caring. It does mean that one needs to let go of the illusion that he is in control of another person. Quite surprisingly, that is all they have to let go of, an illusion. Detachment means that one understands that addiction progresses at the direction of a disease, and family members, no matter how powerful they may be, cannot cause that disease. They cannot cause another person's nervous system to tolerate drugs. A woman may be as mean as the "Wicked Witch of the West," but no act of hers can alter her husband's brain and liver function. Detachment means accepting this.

Detachment means that though one may take heroic measures to protect another from fatal consequences, he cannot control the course of a loved one's addiction. He cannot stop its progression, and he cannot prevent absolutely its consequences.

Detachment means that family members can learn they are not responsible for causing an addict's moods or for resolving them. This is a difficult lesson in a world with songs which encourage us to "make someone happy."

Somehow people have accepted the notion that love is demonstrated by simultaneous suffering. For example, if you really love someone who is in turmoil you too will be in turmoil. It is a notion which alcoholic families need to eschew. Detachment requires that family members learn to not wallow in self-pity because someone else wallows in it, or thrash about agitated just because someone else is agitated and thrashes about. Because an alcoholic is in turmoil does not mean his family has to be in turmoil too.

An addict will never learn that his drug use is compulsive and his behavior drug-affected if his family helps him delude himself into thinking that the family has the problem. In other words, that the problem is communal, caused by the group and shared in the same way by all its members. Difficult though it may be, a family may have to let the alcoholic suffer the pain of his disease alone, while his family gets on with life and enjoys as much as difficult circumstances permit.

Detachment is alien to those who believe that power is control. It is strange to those who think that winning demands fighting. Detachment is foreign and seems at first uncaring and unloving. Sustaining it without support from others is difficult. For this reason alone families find Al-Anon helpful.

Live Life

Families who make the alcoholic the center of their lives are prisoners of addiction. Regardless of how much an addict may want to control the mood at home, his family must avoid sitting around the house silent and moody. A family can enjoy a social life without flaunting it, which would be provocative and enabling, or without making excuses for it. Maintaining that balance takes effort, but it's possible. Spouses are advised to have friends of their own, pursue a job or career, and enjoy hobbies and recreations. Gaining personal autonomy helps prevent one from becoming trapped into enabling out of fear of being abandoned.

Concentrate on Self

To concentrate on changing an alcoholic's behavior is a waste of time. It doesn't work. It can't. To expect someone who is sick to act in a responsible, caring, loving, predictable, mature, attentive and even-tempered way, or to ask a sick person to be less resentful, depressed, bitter, cynical and preoccupied, is doomed to fail because symptoms do not disappear until one treats the disease which causes them. Family members are better off managing their own emotions, dealing with their own frustrations, handling their own fears, and asserting their own needs. In short, family members are better off concentrating on what they can control rather than spending energy on what they cannot control.

Make a list of all the people you can control. Short list, isn't it? Life allows parents the illusion of control until their children reach adolescence. One truth, which takes a long time to learn and needs reinforcing on a regular basis, is that I *control* only myself, my own actions. When I try to control others, they resent it and resist it. I can guide, advise, counsel, urge, encourage, exhort, love, warn, set limits, and even enforce consequences. But I cannot control others. "The knot" goes away only for as long as I accept this.

Confront with Love

If a family decides to wait for an alcoholic to hit bottom, that family might have a very long and very risky wait. To expect someone with a drugged brain and a denying mind to gain insight, overcome denial, stop drinking, and change his ways is to hope for a quartet of miracles.

"Letting go" does not mean remaining mute. New Al-Anon members are advised to "shut up and smile" when things get hot. The advice is intended to help them avoid useless shouting matches, especially when a drunk is drunk. The advice does not mean that a family member should never open his or her mouth. Such silence may prove deadly.

Family members can learn to confront without anger and without malice. In the self help groups, it is called "tough love." Both ingredients are essential. "All love and no tough" is as impotent as "all tough and no love" is provocative. Neither by itself works. Together they have power.

Denial is confronted by specific facts and truthful information. Generalities, such as, "You drink too much," or "You are a mess when you're drunk," are ineffective. In fact, they are counter-productive. Confrontation does not mean yelling into another's face. Confrontation is the process by which one places the truth before another's eyes in a way that makes seeing it unavoidable and compelling. Confrontation simply means telling the truth lovingly, forcefully, concretely and specifically.

A wife confronts with love when she says something as direct and specific as:

> "What I want to say is difficult because I have been hurt and because I care enough not to hurt you. Last week you were drinking and called me a bitch. I was shocked and hurt. I know you are not the kind of person to say such things when you are not drinking. It scares me to see how you change when you drink. You never use language like that when you're not drinking."

To confront in a loving and specific way is to say, for example:

> "You are a smart, responsible person and a good friend. That's why it frightens me to see how drinking affects your memory. Last Friday you agreed to play tennis on Saturday

morning. But you had six drinks, and when I called Saturday you didn't remember the arrangements at all."

A teen-age daughter confronts her mother who has passed out at 6:00 p.m. when she phrases the confrontation this way:

"You promised we would watch the late movie together. By six o'clock you had finished your eighth beer and were asleep. This is the second time this month that has happened. When you drink, you can't keep your promises (and if it is true, adds) I know you are a person who takes promises seriously."

If an alcoholic responds to such confrontations by picking a fight, family members should avoid fighting either by repeating their words or by withdrawing from the encounter in a manner which will not provoke anger. Sometimes it's not easy. "I'm trying to tell you I care enough to help you see how you change when you drink and how it scares me. I'm not here to fight. I don't want to argue. I want you to know what I see."

These or similar words might avoid a fight which, if it happens, is likely to provide the addict an excuse to indulge. At times, no matter what one does, alcoholics will erupt in anger, and family members respond in kind. After all, they are sick.

Family Intervention: Confrontations of the sort mentioned above happen every day in alcoholic homes. The situation can, however, become so troubled and so thick with denial that a more structured intervention is necessary. Family Intervention is a process by which family members learn how to confront an addicted loved one, encourage him to enter treatment, and inform him of the consequences if he refuses. The process is planned, even rehearsed. It cannot be rushed. It is a tool best used as part of a plan and not in a moment of crisis, and it is best directed by a professional willing to spend the time it takes for a family to prepare themselves emotionally. Because intervention requires family members to confront out of love, families need time to get in touch with those feelings, often buried under layers of anger and fear. It is scary, and it involves risk.

It is unrealistic to expect a family member to resolve his anger before confronting. Nevertheless, each member must put his or her anger on hold long enough to confront without anger getting in the way. And if a particular member cannot do this, he should either withdraw from the intervention, or the intervention should be delayed until he can keep his anger in check. Angry interventions end up as enabling, not helpful. Finally, a formal intervention is the most powerful tool a family has. It is not the first choice. Families might want to try other interventions first.

Don't Ask Why

Knowing what causes alcoholism doesn't cure it. Knowing why someone drinks doesn't get it to stop. It is fruitless to ask, "Why?" or "Why me?" Even if such questions were answerable, the answers would not change the facts. What is more productive is figuring out how to confront an alcoholic and how to intervene in the disease as early as possible rather than asking why he got sick in the first place.

Don't Bluff

A person should deliver an ultimatum only if and when he or she is ready, willing and able to carry it out. Don't bluff! Before delivering an "or else," a family member must think through the consequences of the ultimatum and how to deal with them. The family member must be prepared to deal with the addict's response. And they must be capable of carrying out the ultimatum. A spouse, who threatens to leave her husband but has no place to go, delivers an idle threat. And idle threats are enabling. Talking the matter over with a counselor is recommended.

Don't Enable

An exhausted family who has energy for one thing and one thing only should use that energy figuring out how it enables an addict and then stop enabling. Sometimes alcoholics are helped not by what others do, but what they stop doing. Stop rescuing. Stop nagging. Stop covering up. A family which provides financial support to an addict might cut off the funds that support the addiction. One mother decided to ship groceries to her addicted son rather than give him the money to buy them because the money never went for groceries. If a spouse calls work to make an excuse for an alcoholic's absence, the spouse should let the alcoholic make the call for himself. Someone who nags in an effort to get an alcoholic to stop drinking should stop nagging and force the alcoholic to find another excuse to drink besides the nagging. Give him the opportunity to see his compulsion. If someone is tempted to bail an alcoholic out of jail, let him stay. Those who clean up his mess should leave the mess; let him clean it up. An addict will not deal with his addiction until he has to deal with its consequences, and a family which cleans up his mess helps him avoid that. The tough message is this. If you intend to swing on addiction's trapeze, you must know the nets are down.

Don't be the Cure

Families who treat addictive disease with only their own resources, believing that good books, vacations, a return to church, love and chicken soup is the cure, prolong the active disease and its relapses. Addiction and its denial are so complex that one wonders how anyone got sober in the old days when alcoholics were left with both depleted resources and wits. This is not the case today. Professionals treat addiction. Alcoholics Anonymous and Narcotic Anonymous work. When an alcoholic is ready for treatment, the family's job is to get him to treatment and then get help for themselves.

Initially addicts and families recover together by recovering individually, each member participating, each cooperating, each autonomous, and each attending his or her own meetings. It is not a good idea for recovering alcoholics and their spouses to attend the same self-help meetings all the time. They inhibit each other. One censors him or herself when asked to speak. One listens for the other instead of for himself.

Alcoholics do recover without supportive families. Families can recover even while alcoholics drink. The ideal is for both to recover together, but sadly this is not always the case.

Ending a Relationship? There are times when continuing to live with an active alcoholic is destructive and is neither in the best interest of the addict's recovery nor his family's well being. Families are forced to consider whether to end a relationship.

Ending a relationship prematurely may be counter-productive, of course. To sever ties before a family has made at least several attempts to encourage a loved one to enter treatment succeeds only in creating guilt in family members and resentment in addicts. A family loses its self-respect if it makes no such efforts.

It is not easy to determine when to end a relationship. It is unquestionably better to seek counsel in the matter than to let the decision be made by rage or by default. When the health of a family member is at serious risk, one might have to consider ending the relationship as the healthiest thing to do. And when continuing a relationship is itself a factor which enables addiction to continue, then ending that relationship may be necessary. Families ought to seek help with the decision.

Coping with Recovery: Some relationships survive active addiction and get a shot at surviving early recovery, unraveling knots, resolving old feelings and dealing with new ones, learning to live with uncertainty, and coming to grips with the problems recovery itself creates.

In early recovery families fear those changes which might occur when someone gets sober. They wonder if they will like him sober, much less love him. They wonder if he will love them. They fear relapse, or they expect it, especially if it has occurred repeatedly. They might have even become resigned to its inevitability.

Unfortunately, "forgive and forget" is a common idiom in our culture. To forgive is a formidable enough task. For the family who believes that forgetting is essential to forgiving, the task may be impossible. The truth is that one might have to learn to forgive even though he still remembers, and may always remember.

Some families long to return to normal and are shocked when they realize that they have never been "normal," and that alcoholism has been with them as long as they have been a family. Recovery is discovery rather than rediscovery for some.

All too often a family has a mess to clean up. If parents have been conflicted and contradictory about their discipline, children are resentful when parents agree and support each other. Leftover debts may have to be paid. A job may have to be found. Legal problems may need to be resolved. A house may need repair.

A family member who has become accustomed to controlling an alcoholic's moods may not stop immediately. The energy one spends trying to control an alcoholic while he is actively drinking is easily transferred into manipulating his recovery (i.e., coaxing him to attend the right A. A. meetings, finding the right sponsor, working an honest program, participating in group therapy, or to taking Antabuse). Family members walk on eggshells for a while, feeling that they have to navigate around stressful issues in order to prevent relapse. It is no more than the persistence of the illusion of control. It's not easy to let go of another's recovery and concentrate on one's own.

Accepting alcoholism as a disease that makes all members of a family sick, whose treatment is life-long abstinence, and whose recovery means changes in lifestyle and friendships, is no small task.

Mistrust learned from years of hurt and broken promises takes time to rebuild. Trust is regained only through consistency repeated over time. It isn't easy, and it doesn't happen immediately. Trust cannot be forced, and it cannot be faked. It can, however, be relearned even when one is unable to forget the past.

When alcoholism has taught a family how to communicate in silent, indirect, passive or angry ways, learning to communicate directly is unfamiliar, awkward and uncomfortable at first.

Perhaps the most difficult task for a recovering family is recognizing and dealing with feelings. There are old feelings as well as new ones, new fears and new anger, as well as new love and new trust.

The tasks seem formidable. They are. But recovery is not a fantasy. This very day recovery is a fact for millions.

REFERENCES

Alcoholics Anonymous. (1976). *Alcoholics anonymous* (3rd ed.). New York: Alcoholics Anonymous World Services, Inc.

American Medical Association. (1968). *Manual on alcoholism.* Chicago: AMA.

American Psychiatric Association. (1994). *Diagnostic and statistical manual of mental disorder DSM-IV*. Washington, DC: American Psychiatric Association.

American Society of Addiction Medicine and the National Council on Alcoholism and Drug Dependence, Inc. Joint Committee to Study the Definition and Criteria for the Diagnosis of Alcoholism, 4/26/90. (1990). *Alcoholism and alcohol-related problems* (NCADD Fact Sheet). New York: National Council on Alcoholism and Drug Dependence, Inc.

Bangert-Drowns, R. L. (1988). Effects of school-based substance abuse education: A meta-analysis. *Journal of Drug Education*, 18(3), 43-264.

Barnett, M. L. (1955). Alcoholism in the Cantonese of New York City: An anthropological study. In O. Diethelm (Ed.), *Etiology of chronic alcoholism*. Springfield, IL: Charles C. Thomas.

Begleiter, H., Porjesz, B., Bihari, B., & Kissin, B. (1984). Event-related brain potentials in boys at risk for alcoholism. *Science*, 225, 1493-1496.

Blasinsky, M., & Russell, G. K. (Eds.). (1981). Urine testing for marijuana use: Implications for a variety of settings. New York: *The American Council for Marijuana and Other Psychoactive Drugs, Inc.*

Bohman, M. (1978). Some genetic aspects of alcoholism and criminality. *Archives of General Psychiatry*, 35, 269-276.

Bohman, M., Sigvardsson, S., & Cloninger, R. (1981). Maternal inheritance of alcohol abuse. Cross-fostering analysis of adopted women. *Archives of General Psychiatry, 38,* 965-969.

Cadoret, R. J., Troughton, E., O'Gorman, T. W., & Heywood, E. (1986). An adoption study of genetic and environmental factors in drug abuse. *Archives of General Psychiatry, 43,* 1131-1136.

Cadoret, R. J., Cain, C. A., & Grove, W. M. (1980). Development of alcoholism in adoptees raised apart from alcoholic biologic relatives. *Archives of General Psychiatry, 37,* 561-563.

Cloninger, C. R. (1987). Neurogenetic adaptive mechanisms in alcoholism. *Science, 236,* 410-416.

_____. (1988). Etiologic factors in substance abuse: An adoption study perspective. In R. W. Pickens & D. F. Svikis (Eds.), *Biological vulnerability to drug abuse.* National Institute on Drug Abuse Research Monograph 89 (HHS Publication No. (ADM) 88-1590). Rockville, MD: U.S. Department of Health and Human Services.

Drews, T. (1983). *Getting them sober, volume 3.* New Jersey: Bridge Publishing Inc.

Edenburg, H. J. (2003). The collaborative study on the genetics of alcoholism: An update [Electronic version]. *Alcohol Research & Health, 26*(3), 214-218. http://pubs.niaaa.nih.gov/publications/arh26-3/214-218.htm

Edwards, G., Gross, M., Keller, M., Moser, J., & Room, R. (1977). *Alcohol-related disabilities.* Geneva: World Health Organization.

Erickson, C. K. (2007). *The science of addiction: From neurobiology to treatment.* New York: W. W. Norton & Company.

Ewing, J. A., Rouse, B. A., & Pellezzari, E. D. (1974). Alcohol sensitivity and ethnic background. *American Journal of Psychiatry, 131,* 206-210.

Goodwin, D. W. (1976). <u>Is</u> *alcoholism hereditary?* New York: Oxford University Press.

Goodwin, D. W. (1979). Alcoholism and heredity. *Archives of General Psychiatry*, 36, 57-61.

Goodwin, D. W., Schulsinger, F., Hermansen, L., Guze, S. B., & Winokur, G. (1973). Alcohol problems in adoptees raised apart from their alcoholic biologic parents. *Archives of General Psychiatry*, 28, 238-243.

Goodwin, D. W., Schulsinger, F., Moller, N., Hermansen, L., Winokur, G., & Guze, S. B. (1974). Drinking problems in adopted and nonadopted sons of alcoholics. *Archives of General Psychiatry*, 31, 164-169.

Herman, A. I., Philbeck, J. W., Vasilopoulos, N. L., & DePetrello, P. R. (2003). Serotonin transporter promoter polymorphism and differences in alcohol consumption behavior in a college student population. *Alcohol and Alcoholism*, 38(5), 446-449.

Jellinek, E. M. (1960). *The disease concept of alcoholism*. New Haven, CT: Hillhouse Press.

Johnson, V. (1973). *I'll quit tomorrow*. New York: Harper & Row.

Keller, M., McCormick, M., & Efron, V. (1982). *A dictionary of words about alcohol* (2nd ed.). New Brunswick, NJ: Rutgers Center of Alcohol Studies.

Koob, F., & Bloom, F. E. (1988). Cellular and molecular mechanisms of drug dependence. *Science*, 242, 715-723.

Koob, G. F., & LeMoal, M. (1997). Drug abuse: Hedonic and homeostatic dysregulation. *Science*, 278, 52-58.

Korsten, M. A., Matsuzaki, S., Feinman, L., & Lieber, C. S. (1975). High blood acetaldehyde levels after ethanol administration: Difference between alcoholic and nonalcoholic subjects. *New England Journal of Medicine*, 292, 386-389.

Kubler-Ross, E. (1975). *Death: The final stage of growth*. Englewood Cliffs, NJ: Prentice-Hall, Inc.

Lieber, C. S. (1976). The metabolism of alcohol. *Scientific American*, 234, 25-33.

Milam, J., & Ketcham, K. (1981). *Under the influence: A guide to the myths and realities of alcoholism.* Seattle, WA: Madrona Publishers.

Myers, R. D., & Melchior, C. L. (1977). Alcohol drinking: Abnormal intake caused by tetrahydropapaveroline in brain. *Science, 196,* 554-556.

National Council on Alcoholism. (1976). Definition of alcoholism. *Annals of Internal Medicine, 85,* 764.

National Institute on Drug Abuse. (2008). *NIDA InfoFacts: Understanding drug abuse and addiction.* Retrieved from: http://www.drugabuse.gov/Infofacts/understand.html

Peele, S. (1997). Utilizing culture and behaviour in epidemiological models of alcohol consumption and consequences for western nations. *Alcohol & Alcoholism, 32,* 51-64.

Pendery, M. L., Maltzman, I. M., & West, L. J. (1982). Controlled drinking by alcoholics? New findings and a reevaluation of a major affirmative study. *Science, 217,* 169-175.

Pollock, V. E., Volavka, J., Goodwin, D. W., Mednick, S. A., Gabrielli, W. F., Knop, J., & Schulsinger, F. (1983). The EEG after alcohol administration in men at risk for alcoholism. *Archives of General Psychiatry, 40,* 857-861.

Regier, D. A., Farmer, M. E., Rae, D. S., Locke, B. Z., Keith, S. J., Judd, L. L., & Goodwin, F. K. (1990). Comorbidity of mental disorders with alcohol and other drug abuse. *Journal of the American Medical Association, 264*(19), 2511-2518.

Savage, S. R., Joranson, D. E., Covington, E. C., Schnoll, S. H., Heit, H. A., & Gilson, A. M. (2003). Definitions related to the medical use of opioids: Evolution towards universal agreement. *Journal of Pain and Symptom Management, 26*(1), 655-667.

Schuckit, M. A. (1980). Alcoholism and genetics: Possible biological mediators. *Biological Psychicatry, 15,* 437-447.

Schuckit, M. A. (1984) *Drug and alcohol abuse.* New York: Plenum Press.

_____. (1984) Subjective response to alcohol in sons of alcoholics and control subjects. *Archives of General Psychiatry*, 41, 879-884.

Schuckit, M. A., Engstrom, D., Alpert, R., & Duby, J. (1981). Differences in muscle-tension response to ethanol in young men with and without family histories of alcoholism. *Journal of Studies on Alcohol*, 42, 918-924.

Schuckit, M. A., Goodwin, D. W., & Winokur, G. (1972). A study of alcoholism in half siblings. *American Journal of Psychiatry*, 128, 1132.

Schuckit, M. A., & Rayses, V. (1979). *Ethanol ingestion:* Differences in blood acetaldehyde concentrations in relatives of alcoholics and controls. *Science*, 203, 54-55.

Sobell, M. B., & Sobell, L. C. (1973). Alcoholics treated by individualized behavior therapy: One year treatment outcome. *Behavior Research and Therapy*, 11, 599-618.

_____. (1976). Second year treatment outcome of alcoholics treated by individualized behavior therapy: Results. *Behavior Research and Therapy*, 14, 195-215.

_____. (1978). *Behavioral treatment* of *alcohol problems*. New York: Plenum Press.

Thanos, P. K., Volkow, N., Freimuth, P., Umegaki, H., Hiroyuki, I., Roth, G., Ingram, D. K., & Hitzemann, R. (2001). Overexpression of dopamine D2 receptors reduces alcohol self-administration. *Journal of Neurochemistry*, 78(5), 1094-1103.

Thanos, P. K., Taintor, N. B., Rivera, S. N., Umegaki, H., Ikari, H., Roth, G., Ingram, D. K., Hitzemann, R., Fowler, J. S., Gatley, S. J., Wang, G-J, & Volkow, N. D. (2004). DRD2 gene transfer into the nucleus accumbens core of the alcohol preferring and nonpreferring rats attenuates alcohol drinking. *Alcoholism: Clinical & Experimental Research*, 28(5), 720-728.

Vaillant, George. (1983). *The natural history of alcoholism: Causes, patterns, and paths to recovery*. Cambridge, MA: Harvard University Press.

Volkow, N. D., & Fowler, J. S. (2000). Addiction, a disease of compulsion and drive: Involvement of the orbitofrontal cortex. *Cerebral Cortex*, 10(3), 318-325.

Volkow, N. D., Wang, G.-J., Begleiter, H., Porjesz, B., Fowler, J. S., Telang, F., Wong, C., Ma, Y., Logan, J., Goldstein, R., Alexoff, D. & Thanos, P. K. (2006). High levels of dopamine D_2 receptors in unaffected members of alcoholic families: Possible protective factors. *Archives of General Psychiatry*, 63(9), 999-1008.

Wallgren, H., & Barry, III, H. (1970). *Actions of alcohol*. Amsterdam: Elsevier Publishing Co., Inc.

Wegscheider, S. (1981). *Another chance: Hope and health for the alcoholic family*. Palo Alto, CA: Science and Behavior Books, Inc.

Whitfield, C. L., & Williams, K. (1976). *The patient with alcoholism and other drug problems* (4th ed.). Pre-publication

EPILOGUE

An alcoholic doesn't have a drinking problem. His is a "drunking" problem. In other words, the reason an alcoholic picks up a first drink is not as central to his alcohol problem as why he has trouble putting down the tenth one. This particular problem is properly called a disease, a destructive process that defies even heroic efforts at will power to manage it. Believing addiction is a disease is not easy. It is hampered by dozens of myths and misconceptions.

Several longstanding myths cloud our understanding. That alcohol is truth serum is one. Alcohol is a serious, sedative drug; it is a toxin. That alcoholics are bad or weak or irresponsible or crazy is another. A list of our nation's finest includes alcoholic actors, athletes, astronauts, musicians, priests, and politicians. That alcoholism is a moral problem, or a symptom of a psychiatric disorder, are misconceptions; but some still believe those notions. Alcoholism, a drug addiction, is a primary disease, a brain disease. No other name explains why good people, even otherwise healthy people who have integrity and will power, get caught in its grip and head toward incarceration, insanity, and death.

Another misconception is that an "alcoholic personality" is the cause of alcoholism. That myth persists more than twenty years after Dr. George Vaillant's longitudinal study concluded that the alcoholic personality is not the cause of alcoholism, but its result. Addiction does change personality, and that change is, at times, profound. But the term, "personality of addiction" better captures the impact that addiction has on a person's brain, his mind, his feelings, and his spirit than "addictive personality," which suggests a causative or predictive factor.

It is axiomatic of recovery from addiction that no one recovers from a disease he or she does not have. Denial is the most serious barrier to recovery and often requires professional help to overcome it. The other major barrier is hopelessness. Fortunately, for more than seventy years, Alcoholics Anonymous has held out hope for those seeking help.

One oft quoted myth is that peer pressure is what drives teenage drinking and drug use. Actually, the force at work in teenage drinking and drug use is within. The truth is that it is not peer pressure, but peer acceptance, that moves middle school students to drink, and in older teens drinking has more to do with bonding, intense celebrating, and limit pushing than with any sort of pressure either internal or external. The result of "the peer pressure myth" is that it has led to peer resistance programs that do not work because they aim at the wrong target. The unfortunate and unintended side effect of those programs is that they end up demonizing teenager's and their friends.

Not all addiction is of the garden variety type. There are addicts whose drug and alcohol addictions are complicated by other problems: a co-occurring mental illness, chronic pain, and repeated relapse among those complicating factors. Special treatment is necessary in such cases.

A disease produces symptoms, and drug addiction produces symptoms of varying kinds: nervous system signs, social consequence, health problems, and psychological and behavioral problems. Tolerance, loss of control, and persistence despite recurrent problems caused by alcohol and other drugs, indicate a serious problem with alcohol. But addiction does not simply produce symptoms in isolation from each other. Those symptoms occur in a history, one symptom producing the conditions for another symptom, linked together in a dynamic chain of symptoms which is both progressive and predictable. It is that very predictability, despite the variety of personalities to whom it occurs, which provides compelling evidence for thinking of addiction as a disease.

A third barrier to recovery for drug addicts (and this of course includes alcoholics) is that the disease is coupled with an early recovery period, which is distressing, painful and emotionally wrenching for both addicts and their families. A family member, already affected by the active disease, sometimes seriously so, deals in early recovery with his own confusing feelings as well as the raw nervous system of someone newly sober. In early recovery, many are convinced that this disease intends to kill them.

Recovery is not hopeless. It happens every day.